INTEGRATION

UNIVERSITY MATHEMATICAL TEXTS

Determinants and Matrices	A. C. Aitken, D.Sc., F.R.S.
Statistical Mathematics .	A. C. Aitken, D.Sc., F.R.S.
Waves	C. A. Coulson, Ph.D.
Integration	R. P. Gillespie, Ph.D.
Infinite Series	J. M. Hyslop, D.Sc.
Integration of Ordinary Differential Equations	E. L. Ince, D.Sc.
Analytical Geometry of Three Dimensions	Prof. W. H. M'Crea, Ph.D.
Functions of a Complex Variable	E. G. Phillips, M.A., M.Sc.
Vector Methods . .	D. E. Rutherford, Dr. Math.
Theory of Equations	Prof. H. W. Turnbull, F.R.S.

Other volumes in preparation

INTEGRATION

BY

R. P. GILLESPIE, PH.D.

LECTURER IN MATHEMATICS IN
THE UNIVERSITY OF GLASGOW

OLIVER AND BOYD
EDINBURGH AND LONDON
NEW YORK: INTERSCIENCE PUBLISHERS, INC.
1945

FIRST EDITION . . 1939
SECOND EDITION . . 1944
THIRD EDITION . . 1945

PRINTED AND PUBLISHED IN GREAT BRITAIN BY
OLIVER AND BOYD LTD., EDINBURGH

PREFACE

The first four chapters of this book are devoted to an elementary account of integration and demand from the student only a slight knowledge of the differential calculus. The proofs in this part of the book are based on geometrical conceptions, no attempt being made to be rigorous. In Chapter VI an account is given of infinite integrals, and in particular the properties of Gamma and Beta functions are discussed. For a student who desires a working knowledge of the integral calculus Chapters I to IV and Chapter VI cover the most important parts of the ground.

In Chapter V there is a discussion of the Riemann arithmetical definition of the integral, and Chapter VII contains further properties of the Riemann integral as well as a treatment of the Riemann double integral. For these two chapters the student is expected to have a certain amount of knowledge of elementary analysis.

I should like to record my debt of gratitude to my colleagues Miss Margaret S. Black, M.A., Mr T. S. Graham, Ph.D., and Mr J. M. Hyslop, Ph.D., D.Sc., for their generous help in correcting the proofs and for their valuable suggestions. I should also like to thank the general editors of the series for their kindly advice throughout the preparation of the book.

Most of the examples are taken from examination papers set at Glasgow University.

Glasgow, *August* 1939

PREFACE TO THE SECOND EDITION

A CONSIDERABLE number of examples have been added and the chapter on Infinite Integrals has been amplified. I wish to thank my friend Dr T. S. Graham for his helpful suggestions.

R.A.F.,
January 1944

CONTENTS

CHAPTER I

INTRODUCTION

CHAPTER II

INTEGRATION OF ELEMENTARY FUNCTIONS

CHAPTER III

MULTIPLE INTEGRALS

CHAPTER IV

CURVILINEAR AND SURFACE INTEGRALS

CHAPTER V

THE RIEMANN INTEGRAL

CHAPTER VI

INFINITE INTEGRALS

CHAPTER VII

THE RIEMANN DOUBLE INTEGRAL

CHAPTER I

INTRODUCTION

§ 1. THE integral calculus may be said to have been begun by the Greek mathematicians who strove to evaluate the area of a circle. The area of a rectangle is equal to the product of its length and breadth, and from this, by the methods of Euclid, the areas of figures bounded by straight lines can be determined. These methods are not applicable in the case of a circle or of any figure bounded by a curve. If n-sided regular polygons are inscribed in and circumscribed about a circle, their areas can be calculated by Euclidean methods, and it is clear that the area of the circle lies between these two areas. As n increases the difference between the two areas becomes smaller, and we can make this difference as small as we please by choosing n sufficiently large. Thus we have a method which yields the area of the circle to any degree of accuracy that is required. This method is essentially that of the integral calculus. In the language of the calculus we say that the area of the circle is the *limit* for n tending to infinity of the area of the regular n-sided inscribed or circumscribed polygon.

An equivalent method of evaluating the area of a circle and one which is capable of extension to the evaluation of other areas is that illustrated in Fig. 1.

OAB is that part of the circle $x^2+y^2 = a^2$ which lies in the first quadrant, and OA is divided into n equal parts by points H, K, ..., M, N, ..., V. Through these points ordinates are drawn to meet the circle, and a set of rectangles is formed by drawing parallels like QR, PS to the x-axis. Let $\mathbf{S}$ denote the sum of the areas of the n

rectangles like $MNSP$ and **s** denote the sum of the areas of the n rectangles like $MNQR$. Then the area of the circle

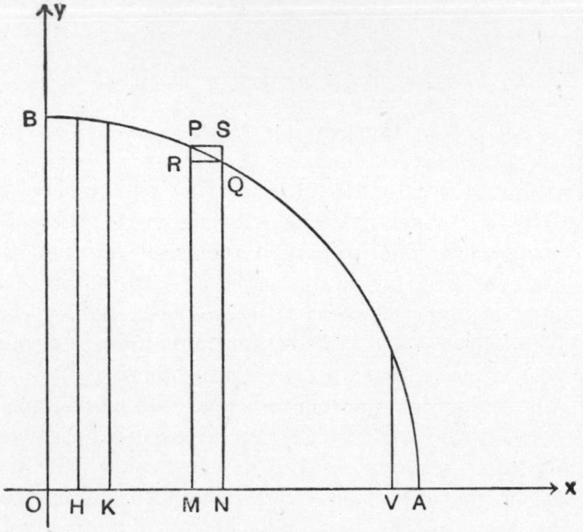

FIG. 1.

lies between **4S** and 4**s**, and as n tends to infinity the difference between **S** and **s** tends to zero ; thus the area of the circle is the common limit of **4S** and 4**s**.

§ 2. Areas.

We shall now proceed to show that this method may be extended to evaluate other types of areas. Let $f(x)$ be a function which is positive for values of x lying between a and b, where $a<b$. We wish to evaluate the area $ABDC$ (Fig. 2) enclosed by the curve $y = f(x)$ and the lines $x = a$, $x = b$, $y = 0$. It is clear that the circle problem of § 1 is the special case of this general problem where $f(x) = \sqrt{(a^2-x^2)}$ and the interval (a, b) is $(0, a)$.

Let M be a variable point of abscissa x, on the x-axis between A and B, and let the ordinate at M meet the curve CD in P. If z denotes the variable area $AMPC$, it is clear that z varies as M changes its position on the x-axis; i.e. z is a function of x, the abscissa of M. Also when $x = a$, $z = 0$, and the required area $ABDC$ is the value of z when $x = b$.

We now proceed to discuss the rate at which z varies when x varies or, using the language of the differential calculus, we try to find dz/dx. We take a point N near M on the x-axis of abscissa $x + \Delta x$, erect an ordinate NQ

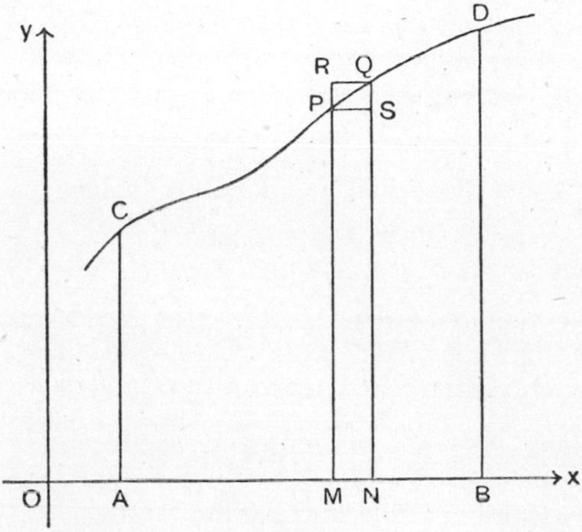

FIG. 2.

to meet the curve and complete the rectangles $MNSP$ and $MNQR$ as in the case of the circle in Fig. 1. As the variable x takes the increment Δx, let the resulting increment of z be Δz, so that $z + \Delta z$ is the area $ANQC$ and Δz is the area between the lines MP, NQ, MN and the arc PQ of the curve.

If Δx is sufficiently small it is clear that the area Δz lies between the areas of the rectangles $MNSP$ and $MNQR$, i.e. between $MP \,.\, \Delta x$ and $NQ \,.\, \Delta x$.* Hence

* In order to make this treatment rigorous we should require to discuss the properties of the function $f(x)$. A rigorous discussion will be given in Chapter V.

$\Delta z/\Delta x$ lies between MP and NQ. Now let Δx become smaller and smaller; N approaches M and NQ becomes more and more nearly equal to MP. We say that the *limit* of $\Delta z/\Delta x$ as Δx tends to zero is MP, and the limit of $\Delta z/\Delta x$ as $\Delta x \to 0$ is dz/dx, the derivative of the function z with respect to x. We write

$$\lim_{\Delta x \to 0} \frac{\Delta z}{\Delta x} = \frac{dz}{dx} = MP = f(x).$$

Thus the function z is such that its derivative is $f(x)$ and its value is zero when $x = a$. If we can find *any* function $F(x)$ whose derivative is $f(x)$, then z must be of the form

$$z(x) = F(x) + \text{constant}.$$

Now we know that when $x = a$, $z = 0$; hence

$$0 = F(a) + \text{constant},$$

and so

$$z(x) = F(x) - F(a).$$

Since the required area $ABDC$ is the value of z when $x = b$, it is given by $F(b) - F(a)$. This is called **the integral of f(x) with respect to x from a to b,** and is written

$$\int_a^b f(x)\,dx,$$

The expression $F(b) - F(a)$ is often written $[F(x)]_a^b$. This value for the area $ABDC$ is clearly positive since $z = 0$ when $x = a$ and $dz/dx = f(x) > 0$. We see that the problem of evaluating the area under the curve $y = f(x)$ reduces to that of finding a function $F(x)$ whose derivative is $f(x)$. This process of finding a function $F(x)$ whose derivative is $f(x)$ is called the process of **integration** of $f(x)$ with respect to x. Any function $F(x)$ whose derivative is $f(x)$ is said to be an **indefinite integral** of $f(x)$, and $f(x)$ is called the **integrand**. It is clear that any two indefinite integrals of $f(x)$ differ only by a constant, and in general we write

$$\int f(x)dx = F(x) + A,$$

where A is called the **constant of integration.**

The expression for the area, $\int_a^b f(x)dx$, is called a **definite integral**, and a, b are called the **limits of integration**. It should be noted that the symbol $\int \ldots dx$ is *one* symbol.

If $f(x)$ is negative the curve $y = f(x)$ lies below the x-axis, and the curve $y = -f(x)$ lying above the x-axis is the reflection of the curve $y = f(x)$ in the x-axis. Now by the above discussion the area between the curve $y = -f(x)$ and the lines $x = a$, $x = b$, $y = 0$ is given by

$$\int_a^b \left[-f(x)\right]dx = F(a)-F(b) = -\int_a^b f(x)dx.$$

Thus when $f(x)$ is negative the formula for the area between the curve $y = f(x)$ and the x-axis, $\int_a^b f(x)dx$, gives the correct numerical value for the area *but with a negative sign*. If we make the convention that areas under the x-axis have negative sign, the area between the curve $y = f(x)$ and the x-axis is always given by $\int_a^b f(x)dx$.

Ex. 1. To find the area of a circle of radius a.

The area of the first quadrant of the circle $x^2+y^2 = a^2$ is given by $\int_0^a \sqrt{(a^2-x^2)}dx$. Thus the problem is to find a function whose derivative is $\sqrt{(a^2-x^2)}$. We shall show later that such a function is

$$F(x) \equiv \frac{x}{2}\sqrt{(a^2-x^2)} + \frac{a^2}{2}\sin^{-1}\left(\frac{x}{a}\right);$$

hence $\int_0^a \sqrt{(a^2-x^2)}dx = F(a)-F(0) = \frac{a^2}{2}\sin^{-1} 1 = \frac{\pi a^2}{4}$.

Thus the area of the circle is πa^2.

Ex. 2. To find the area between the curve $y = x(x^2-1)$ and the x-axis.

It can be easily verified that an indefinite integral of the function $x(x^2-1)$ is $x^4/4-x^2/2$. The area between the curve and the x-axis consists of a part between $x=-1$ and $x=0$ which lies above the x-axis and a part between $x=0$ and $x=1$ which lies below the x-axis. The first area is $\left[\frac{x^4}{4}-\frac{x^2}{2}\right]_{-1}^{0}=\frac{1}{4}$ and the second is $\left[\frac{x^4}{4}-\frac{x^2}{2}\right]_{0}^{1}=-\frac{1}{4}$. This illustrates the convention that areas above the x-axis are positive and areas below negative.

Ex. 3. To evaluate the integral $\int_3^7 \sqrt{(7+6x-x^2)}dx$.

If $y=\sqrt{(7+6x-x^2)}$, then $x^2+y^2-6x-7=0$, which is the equation of the circle with centre (3, 0) and radius 4. Hence the integral represents the area of a quadrant of a circle of radius 4 ; *i.e.*

$$\int_3^7 \sqrt{(7+6x-x^2)}dx = 4\pi.$$

§ 3. The Integral as the Limit of a Sum

In § 1 we saw that the area of a circle is the limit of a sum of areas of rectangles. This is the principle which lies behind the process of the last paragraph. Let the segment AB in Fig. 2 be divided into n parts, not necessarily equal, by points whose abscissæ are $x_0, x_1, x_2, \ldots, x_n$, where $a=x_0<x_1<x_2<\ldots<x_n=b$, and let ordinates be drawn through these points to meet the curve. Let M, N denote the points of abscissæ x_{r-1}, x_r, and let ξ_r be the abscissa of any point in MN. Then $f(\xi_r)\,.\,(x_r-x_{r-1})$ is the area of the rectangle on the base MN whose height is the ordinate at the point ξ_r. If the sum of the areas of all such rectangles is taken an area is obtained which is approximately the area $ABDC$; and by letting n increase so that the greatest of the lengths x_r-x_{r-1} becomes smaller, this area becomes more and more nearly equal to the area $ABDC$. We say that the limit of this sum of areas is the area $ABDC$, which we have shown to be $\int_a^b f(x)dx$. We write

$$\lim_{n\to\infty} \sum_{r=1}^{n} f(\xi_r)\,.\,(x_r-x_{r-1}) = \int_a^b f(x)dx,$$

where, as n tends to infinity, each $x_r - x_{r-1}$ tends to zero and ξ_r is *any* point in the interval (x_{r-1}, x_r).*

§ 4. Volumes of Revolution

We can employ the limiting process of § 2 to evaluate the volume enclosed by a surface of revolution. Let the arc *CPD* of the curve $y = f(x)$ in Fig. 2 rotate about the x-axis so that we have a solid figure bounded by a surface of revolution and two planes perpendicular to the axis of revolution. Let V denote the volume of the figure traced out by the area *AMPC*; then V is clearly a function $V(x)$ of the abscissa x of M. Let $V + \Delta V$ be the volume of the figure traced out by *ANQC*, so that ΔV is the slice of the solid figure which is obtained by rotating *PQ*. Then it is clear that ΔV lies between the volumes of the circular cylinders obtained by rotating the rectangles *MNSP* and *MNQR* about the x-axis. These volumes are respectively $\pi(MP)^2\Delta x$ and $\pi(NQ)^2\Delta x$. Hence $\Delta V/\Delta x$ lies between $\pi(MP)^2$ and $\pi(NQ)^2$. As before let $\Delta x \to 0$; then $NQ \to MP$ and $\Delta V/\Delta x \to dV/dx$. Thus $dV/dx = \pi[f(x)]^2$ and, since $V = 0$ when $x = a$, the volume traced out by *ABDC* is given by

$$\pi \int_a^b y^2 dx,$$

where $y = f(x)$.

Ex. 1. To find the volume of the sphere of radius a.

We rotate about the x-axis the quadrant *OAB* of the circle $x^2 + y^2 = a^2$, (Fig. 1). Then the volume of the sphere is $2\pi \int_0^a y^2 dx = 2\pi \int_0^a (a^2 - x^2) dx$. Now the function $(a^2x - x^3/3)$ is such that its derivative is $(a^2 - x^2)$; hence the volume of the sphere is $2\pi \left[a^2x - \frac{1}{3}x^3\right]_0^a = \frac{4}{3}\pi a^3$.

Ex. 2. To find the volume cut off a paraboloid of revolution by a plane perpendicular to the axis of revolution.

* This treatment is of course not rigorous. A complete account of this definition of the integral is given in Chapter V.

Let the paraboloid be that obtained by revolving the parabola $y^2 = 4ax$ about the x-axis, and the plane that perpendicular to the x-axis through the point $(h, 0)$. The volume of this section is clearly $\pi\int_0^h y^2dx = \pi\int_0^h 4ax\,dx$, and, since $\frac{d}{dx}\,2ax^2 = 4ax$, this is $\pi\Big[2ax^2\Big]_0^h = 2\pi ah^2$.

§ 5. Properties of the Integral

From the definition of the integral as an area given in § 2 we can deduce certain fundamental properties of the integral.

(i) $$\int_b^a f(x)dx = -\int_a^b f(x)dx.$$

Let $F(x)$ be an indefinite integral of $f(x)$. Then

$$\int_b^a f(x)dx = \Big[F(x)\Big]_b^a = F(a) - F(b) = -\Big[F(x)\Big]_a^b = -\int_a^b f(x)dx.$$

(ii) $$\int_a^c f(x)dx + \int_c^b f(x)dx = \int_a^b f(x)dx.$$

For,

$$\int_a^c f(x)dx + \int_c^b f(x)dx = F(c) - F(a) + F(b) - F(c)$$
$$= F(b) - F(a) = \int_a^b f(x)dx.$$

(iii) $$\int_a^b [f(x)+g(x)]dx = \int_a^b f(x)dx + \int_a^b g(x)dx.$$

This follows at once since

$$\int_a^b [f(x)+g(x)]dx = \Big[F(x)+G(x)\Big]_a^b$$
$$= F(b)+G(b)-F(a)-G(a)$$
$$= [F(b)-F(a)]+[G(b)-G(a)]$$
$$= \int_a^b f(x)dx + \int_a^b g(x)dx,$$

where $G(x)$ is an indefinite integral of $g(x)$.

CHAPTER II

INTEGRATION OF ELEMENTARY FUNCTIONS

§ 6. An indefinite integral of a given function $f(x)$ is a function $F(x)$ whose derivative is $f(x)$. Having found an indefinite integral $F(x)$ we can at once write down the value $F(b)-F(a)$ of the definite integral $\int_a^b f(x)dx$. Thus the first step in the evaluation of a definite integral is the attempt to find an indefinite integral of the integrand. From this point of view integration is simply the inverse of differentiation. The purpose of the present chapter is to collect a set of results on the integration of elementary functions.

The process is much more haphazard than the corresponding one for differentiation and the number of cases in which simple rules for integration can be given is exceedingly small. There are quite simple functions, for example e^{x^2}, which cannot be integrated in terms of the ordinary functions at all, and their integrals may be used to define new functions which are not expressible in terms of known functions. We shall use two general methods in the course of the work, *change of variable* and *integration by parts*, but even when these methods may be used individual cases demand individual treatment. We begin by giving a table of standard integrals, the results following at once from the corresponding rules of differentiation.

§ 7. Standard Integrals

1. $\dfrac{d}{dx} x^n = nx^{n-1}$, $\quad \displaystyle\int \mathbf{x^n dx = \frac{1}{n+1} x^{n+1}, n \neq -1.}$

2. $\dfrac{d}{dx} \log x = \dfrac{1}{x}$, $\quad \displaystyle\int \frac{\mathbf{dx}}{\mathbf{x}} = \mathbf{\log |x|.}$ — note |x|.

3. $\dfrac{d}{dx} e^{kx} = ke^{kx}$, $\quad \displaystyle\int \mathbf{e^{kx} dx = \frac{1}{k} e^{kx}.}$

4. $\dfrac{d}{dx} \sin x = \cos x$, $\quad \displaystyle\int \mathbf{\cos x \, dx = \sin x.}$

5. $\dfrac{d}{dx} \cos x = -\sin x$, $\quad \displaystyle\int \mathbf{\sin x \, dx = -\cos x.}$

6. $\dfrac{d}{dx} \tan x = \sec^2 x$, $\quad \displaystyle\int \mathbf{\sec^2 x \, dx = \tan x.}$

7. $\dfrac{d}{dx} \cot x = -\operatorname{cosec}^2 x$, $\quad \displaystyle\int \mathbf{\operatorname{cosec}^2 x \, dx = -\cot x.}$

8. $\dfrac{d}{dx} \sinh x = \cosh x$, $\quad \displaystyle\int \mathbf{\cosh x \, dx = \sinh x.}$

9. $\dfrac{d}{dx} \cosh x = \sinh x$, $\quad \displaystyle\int \mathbf{\sinh x \, dx = \cosh x.}$

10. $\dfrac{d}{dx} \tanh x = \operatorname{sech}^2 x$, $\quad \displaystyle\int \mathbf{\operatorname{sech}^2 x \, dx = \tanh x.}$

11. $\dfrac{d}{dx} \coth x = -\operatorname{cosech}^2 x$, $\quad \displaystyle\int \mathbf{\operatorname{cosech}^2 x \, dx = -\coth x.}$

12. $\dfrac{d}{dx} \sin^{-1} \dfrac{x}{a} = \dfrac{1}{\sqrt{(a^2-x^2)}}$, $\quad \displaystyle\int \mathbf{\frac{dx}{\sqrt{(a^2-x^2)}} = \sin^{-1} \frac{x}{a}}$

$\dfrac{d}{dx} \cos^{-1} \dfrac{x}{a} = \dfrac{-1}{\sqrt{(a^2-x^2)}}$, $\quad$ or $\mathbf{= -\cos^{-1} \dfrac{x}{a}.}$

13. $\dfrac{d}{dx} \tan^{-1} \dfrac{x}{a} = \dfrac{a}{x^2+a^2}$, $\quad \displaystyle\int \mathbf{\frac{dx}{x^2+a^2} = \frac{1}{a} \tan^{-1} \frac{x}{a}.}$

14. $\frac{d}{dx}\log|x\pm\sqrt{(x^2+a^2)}|$ $\qquad \int\frac{\mathbf{dx}}{\pm\sqrt{(\mathbf{x}^2+\mathbf{a}^2)}}$

$$= \frac{d}{dx}\pm\sinh^{-1}\frac{x}{a} \qquad = \mathbf{\log|x\pm\sqrt{(x^2+a^2)}|}$$

$$= \frac{1}{\pm\sqrt{(x^2+a^2)}}, \qquad \text{or} = \pm\mathbf{\sinh^{-1}\frac{x}{a}}.$$

15. $\frac{d}{dx}\log[x\pm\sqrt{(x^2-a^2)}]$ $\qquad \int\frac{\mathbf{dx}}{\pm\sqrt{(\mathbf{x}^2-\mathbf{a}^2)}}$

$$= \frac{d}{dx}\pm\cosh^{-1}\frac{x}{a} \qquad = \mathbf{\log|x\pm\sqrt{(x^2-a^2)}|}$$

$$= \frac{1}{\pm\sqrt{(x^2-a^2)}}, \qquad \text{or} = \pm\mathbf{\cosh^{-1}\left|\frac{x}{a}\right|}.$$

16. $\frac{d}{dx}\frac{1}{2a}\log\frac{a+x}{a-x}$ $\qquad \int\frac{\mathbf{dx}}{\mathbf{a^2-x^2}} = \mathbf{\frac{1}{2a}\log\frac{a+x}{a-x}}$

$$= \frac{d}{dx}\frac{1}{a}\tanh^{-1}\frac{x}{a},\ |x|<a, \qquad = \mathbf{\frac{1}{a}\tanh^{-1}\frac{x}{a},\ |x|<a,}$$

$$= \frac{d}{dx}\frac{1}{2a}\log\frac{x+a}{x-a} \qquad = \mathbf{\frac{1}{2a}\log\frac{x+a}{x-a}}$$

$$= \frac{d}{dx}\frac{1}{a}\coth^{-1}\frac{x}{a},\ |x|>a>0, \qquad = \mathbf{\frac{1}{a}\coth^{-1}\frac{x}{a},}$$

$$= \frac{1}{a^2-x^2}, \qquad \mathbf{|x|>a>0.}$$

Notes

The result $\int\frac{dx}{x} = \log|x|$ requires some explanation. In the statement $d/dx\,[\log x] = 1/x$ it is implied that x is positive, since the logarithm of a negative number is not real; hence the corresponding result $\int\frac{dx}{x} = \log x$ is only true for positive values of x. If x is negative $\log(-x)$ is real and $d/dx\,[\log(-x)] = 1/x$, so that when x is negative

$\int \frac{dx}{x} = \log(-x)$. Both results are therefore included in the displayed formula $\int \frac{dx}{x} = \log |x|$.

This result may be used as a definition of the logarithm. We may define $\log x$ to be

$$\int_1^x \frac{dt}{t},$$

and the usual properties of the logarithmic function can be deduced from this definition.

The inverse trigonometric functions in formulæ 12, 13 are single-valued functions; $\sin^{-1} x$, $\tan^{-1} x$ are the angles lying between $-\pi/2$ and $\pi/2$ whose sine and tangent are x, $\cos^{-1} x$ is the angle lying between 0 and π whose cosine is x. This is most important in the evaluation of definite integrals. The following alternative notation is often used: arc sin x denotes $\sin^{-1} x$, arc tan $x = \tan^{-1} x$, etc.

The inverse hyperbolic function $\cosh^{-1} \left|\frac{x}{a}\right|$ in formula 15 is a single-valued function; it is the *positive* number y such that $\left|\frac{x}{a}\right| = \cosh y$.

The function a^x may be integrated by writing it as $e^{x \log a}$.

§ 8. Change of Variable

This is the first of the two general methods of integration mentioned in § 6. Let $x = \phi(u)$ where $\phi(u)$ is a single-valued function of u and the problem is to express the integral of a function $f(x)$ with respect to x as the integral of a function of u with respect to the variable u. Let $F(x)$ be an indefinite integral of $f(x)$, so that $d/dxF(x) = f(x)$. Now

$$\frac{du}{dx} \frac{d}{du} F[\phi(u)] = f[\phi(u)],$$

i.e. $$\frac{d}{du} F[\phi(u)] = f[\phi(u)]\phi'(u), \text{ and so}$$

$$F[\phi(u)] = \int f[\phi(u)]\phi'(u)du.$$

But $$F[\phi(u)] = F(x) = \int f(x)dx, \text{ giving finally}$$

$$\int \mathbf{f(x)dx} = \int \mathbf{f[\phi(u)]\phi'(u)du}.$$

Thus the rule is : **to transform the integral by means of the substitution $\mathbf{x} = \phi(\mathbf{u})$ express the integrand in terms of the new variable u and replace dx by $\phi'(\mathbf{u})\mathbf{du}$.**

It follows that we can transform the definite integral $\int_a^b f(x)dx$ into a definite integral with respect to the variable u. If the equation $x = \phi(u)$ is solvable for u as a single-valued function of x and if $a = \phi(c)$, $b = \phi(d)$, i.e. if $u = c$ when $x = a$ and $u = d$ when $x = b$, we have the result

$$\int_a^b f(x)dx = \int_c^d f[\phi(u)]\phi'(u)du.$$

By the use of change of variable we can extend the standard forms given in the last paragraph to slightly more general cases. In $\int (ax+b)^n dx$ let $u = ax+b$, so that $du = a\,dx$, giving $\frac{1}{a}\int u^n du = \frac{1}{(n+1)a} u^{n+1} = \frac{1}{(n+1)a}(ax+b)^{n+1}$, $n \neq -1$. Similarly we can show that the integral of $\sin(ax+b)$ is $(-1/a)\cos(ax+b)$, the integral of $\cos(ax+b)$ is $(1/a)\sin(ax+b)$, and so on.

An important special case is the integral of $\phi'(x)/\phi(x)$; let $\phi(x) = u$, so that

$$\int \frac{\phi'(x)}{\phi(x)}dx = \int \frac{du}{u} = \log|u| = \log|\phi(x)|.$$

Examples of this case are the following :

$$\int \tan x\, dx = -\log|\cos x|, \quad \int \tanh x\, dx = \log \cosh x,$$

$$\int \cot x\, dx = \log|\sin x|, \quad \int \coth x\, dx = \log|\sinh x|.$$

The result

$$\int_0^a f(x)dx = \int_0^a f(a-x)dx,$$

which follows at once by putting $x = a-u$ in the first integral, is important in the evaluation of some definite integrals.

Ex. From the integral definition of the logarithm (see page 12) prove that

$$\log xy = \log x + \log y.$$

§ 9. Integration by Parts

This important method follows at once from the rule for the differentiation of a product :

$$\frac{d}{dx}[u(x)v(x)] = u'(x)v(x) + u(x)v'(x).$$

Hence

$$\int [u'(x)v(x) + u(x)v'(x)]dx = u(x)v(x), \text{ so that}$$

$$\int u'(x)v(x)dx = u(x)v(x) - \int u(x)v'(x)dx.$$

Thus

$$\int f(x)g(x)dx = F(x)g(x) - \int F(x)g'(x)dx,$$

where $F(x)$ is an indefinite integral of $f(x)$.

For definite integrals it follows that

$$\int_a^b f(x)g(x)dx = \Big[F(x)g(x)\Big]_a^b - \int_a^b F(x)g'(x)dx.$$

It often happens that it is impossible to integrate directly the function $f(x)g(x)$, while it is possible to integrate $f(x)$ and $F(x)g'(x)$, thus giving a method of integrating $f(x)g(x)$. As an example let us take the function $x \cos x$, which cannot be integrated directly. When we apply the integration by parts formula, taking $f(x) \equiv \cos x$, $g(x) \equiv x$, we have

$$\int x \cos x \, dx = x \sin x - \int \sin x \, dx = x \sin x + \cos x.$$

Ex. Use the method of integration by parts to prove that

$$\text{(i)} \int \log x \, dx = x \log x - x, \quad \text{(ii)} \int \frac{\log x}{x} dx = \tfrac{1}{2}(\log x)^2.$$

The following are some important functions which can be integrated using the method of integration by parts:

$$(1) \qquad \int \sqrt{(a^2-x^2)}dx, \quad x^2 < a^2.$$

In this case we take $f(x) \equiv 1$, $g(x) \equiv \sqrt{(a^2-x^2)}$, giving

$$\int \sqrt{(a^2-x^2)}dx = x\sqrt{(a^2-x^2)} - \int x \,.\, \frac{-x}{\sqrt{(a^2-x^2)}} dx.$$

Now

$$\int \frac{x^2}{\sqrt{(a^2-x^2)}} dx = \int \left[\frac{-(a^2-x^2)}{\sqrt{(a^2-x^2)}} + \frac{a^2}{\sqrt{(a^2-x^2)}} \right] dx$$

$$= -\int \sqrt{(a^2-x^2)}dx + a^2 \sin^{-1} \frac{x}{a}.$$

Hence

$$\int \sqrt{(a^2-x^2)}dx = \frac{x}{2}\sqrt{(a^2-x^2)} + \frac{a^2}{2} \sin^{-1} \frac{x}{a}.$$

(2) Similarly it can be shown that

$$\int \sqrt{(x^2+a^2)}dx = \frac{x}{2} \sqrt{(x^2+a^2)} + \frac{a^2}{2} \log [x + \sqrt{(x^2+a^2)}],$$

$$\int \sqrt{(x^2-a^2)}dx = \frac{x}{2} \sqrt{(x^2-a^2)} - \frac{a^2}{2} \log |x + \sqrt{(x^2-a^2)}|.$$

$$(3) \qquad \int e^{ax} \cos (bx+c)dx, \quad \int e^{ax} \sin (bx+c)dx.$$

By integration by parts,

$$\int e^{ax} \cos (bx+c)dx = \frac{1}{a} e^{ax} \cos (bx+c) + \frac{b}{a}\int e^{ax} \sin (bx+c)dx,$$

$$\int e^{ax} \sin (bx+c)dx = \frac{1}{a} e^{ax} \sin (bx+c) - \frac{b}{a}\int e^{ax} \cos (bx+c)dx,$$

and, on solving these two equations for the required integrals, we obtain

$$\int \mathbf{e^{ax} \cos (bx+c)dx = \frac{e^{ax}}{a^2+b^2}[a \cos (bx+c)+b \sin (bx+c)]},$$

$$\int \mathbf{e^{ax} \sin (bx+c)dx = \frac{e^{ax}}{a^2+b^2}[a \sin (bx+c)-b \cos (bx+c)]}.$$

§ 10. Integration of Rational Functions

A rational function of x is a function of the form $f(x)/g(x)$, when $f(x)$ and $g(x)$ are polynomials in x. We shall assume that $f(x)$ is of lower degree than $g(x)$, for, if this is not so, the function can be expressed as the sum of a polynomial in x and a rational function in which the numerator is of lower degree than the denominator ; *e.g.*

$$\frac{x^3}{x^2+1} = x - \frac{x}{x^2+1}.$$

The rational function can always be expressed as a sum of partial fractions * of the types :

(i) $\dfrac{A}{(x+a)^r}$, $r = 1, 2, 3, \ldots$;

(ii) $\dfrac{Ax+B}{(ax^2+bx+c)^r}$, $b^2 < 4ac$, $r = 1, 2, 3, \ldots$.

Thus the integration of a rational function reduces to the integration of these partial fractions.

(i) $\displaystyle\int \frac{dx}{x+a} = \log |x+a|$,

* Turnbull, *Theory of Equations*, § 19.

$$\int \frac{dx}{(x+a)^r} = \frac{-1}{r-1}\frac{1}{(x+a)^{r-1}},\ r = 2, 3, \ldots .$$

(ii) We break up the partial fraction as follows :

$$\frac{Ax+B}{(ax^2+bx+c)^r} = \frac{A}{2a}\frac{2ax+b}{(ax^2+bx+c)^r} + \left(B-\frac{Ab}{2a}\right)\frac{1}{(ax^2+bx+c)^r};$$

and

$$\int \frac{2ax+b}{(ax^2+bx+c)^r}\,dx = \frac{-1}{r-1}\frac{1}{(ax^2+bx+c)^{r-1}},\ r = 2, 3, \ldots ,$$

$$\text{or} = \log|ax^2+bx+c|,\ r = 1.$$

It is clear that we have now only to integrate functions of the type $1/(ax^2+bx+c)^r$. We write ax^2+bx+c in the form $a[(x-p)^2+q^2]$, where $p = -b/2a$, $q^2 = (4ac-b^2)/4a^2$, and let $u = x-p$, so that the integral reduces to the type $\int \frac{dx}{(x^2+q^2)^r}$. When $r = 1$, this is $(1/q)\tan^{-1}(x/q)$. If $r > 1$, we may proceed as follows :

$$I_r = \int \frac{dx}{(x^2+q^2)^r} = \frac{1}{q^2}\int \frac{(x^2+q^2)-x^2}{(x^2+q^2)^r}\,dx$$

$$= \frac{1}{q^2}I_{r-1} - \frac{1}{q^2}\int \frac{x^2dx}{(x^2+q^2)^r}$$

$$= \frac{1}{q^2}I_{r-1} + \frac{x}{2(r-1)q^2(x^2+q^2)^{r-1}} - \frac{1}{2(r-1)q^2}I_{r-1},$$

by integration by parts. Hence

$$I_r = \frac{x}{2(r-1)q^2(x^2+q^2)^{r-1}} + \frac{2r-3}{2(r-1)q^2}I_{r-1}.$$

This is called a *Reduction Formula*, a formula which reduces the evaluation of I_r to that of I_{r-1}. A repeated use of this formula reduces the integration of $(x^2+q^2)^{-r}$ to that of $(x^2+q^2)^{-1}$, one of the standard forms.

Thus, summing up, we see that *the integration of a rational function can always be performed*, since we have reduced the process to the integration of standard types.

An alternative method of discussing the integral of $1/(x^2+q^2)^r$ is to use the transformation $x = q \tan \theta$, giving

$$\int \frac{dx}{(x^2+q^2)^r} = q^{1-2r} \int (\cos \theta)^{2r-2} d\theta.$$

In the next paragraph we shall obtain a reduction formula for the integral of $\cos^n \theta$. This trigonometric substitution is very useful in the case of definite integrals.

Ex. 1. Integrate the functions *

$$\text{(i)} \quad \frac{1}{(x-1)^2\,(x^2+x+1)}, \quad \text{(ii)} \quad \frac{5x+2}{x^3-8}.$$

Ex. 2. Show that

$$\int_0^1 \frac{1-x^2}{1+x^2+x^4}\, dx = \frac{1}{2} \log 3.$$

§ 11. Integration of Trigonometric Functions

(1) The products $\sin mx \cos nx$, $\cos mx \cos nx$, $\sin mx \sin nx$ may be integrated by expressing them as sums and differences of sines and cosines, *e.g.*:

$$\int \sin mx \cos nx\, dx = \frac{1}{2}\int [\sin (m+n)x + \sin (m-n)x] dx$$

$$= -\frac{1}{2}\left[\frac{\cos (m+n)x}{m+n} + \frac{\cos (m-n)x}{m-n}\right], m \neq n.$$

* Here as elsewhere the value of an indefinite integral should be checked by differentiation. It is not convenient to give answers as an indefinite integral can sometimes be expressed in several ways which have no obvious similarity ;

e.g. $\tan^{-1} (\sinh x)$, $2 \tan^{-1} e^x$, $2 \tan^{-1} \left(\tanh \frac{x}{2}\right)$, $\sin^{-1} (\tanh x)$ are all indefinite integrals of $\operatorname{sech} x$.

(2) The functions $\cos^2 nx$, $\sin^2 nx$ may be integrated by integration by parts or by expressing them as $\frac{1}{2}(1 \pm \cos 2nx)$. The results are

$$\int \cos^2 nx\, dx = \frac{x}{2} + \frac{1}{4n}\sin 2nx.$$

$$\int \sin^2 nx\, dx = \frac{x}{2} - \frac{1}{4n}\sin 2nx.$$

(3) If n is a positive integer $\cos^n x$, $\sin^n x$ can be expressed as sums of sines and cosines of multiples of x by the methods of De Moivre's Theorem, and can thus be integrated. Alternatively we may derive a formula of reduction which, as we shall see, is most useful in the case of definite integrals.

Let $$I_n = \int \cos^n x\, dx = \int \cos^{n-1} x \cos x\, dx$$

$$= \sin x \cos^{n-1} x + (n-1)\int \sin^2 x \cos^{n-2} x\, dx$$

$$= \sin x \cos^{n-1} x + (n-1)I_{n-2} - (n-1)I_n\,;$$

and thus we have the reduction formula

$$\int \cos^n x\, dx = \frac{\sin x \cos^{n-1} x}{n} + \frac{n-1}{n}\int \cos^{n-2} x\, dx.$$

Similarly we obtain the formula:

$$\int \sin^n x\, dx = -\frac{\cos x \sin^{n-1} x}{n} + \frac{n-1}{n}\int \sin^{n-2} x\, dx.$$

In these formulæ n need not be a positive integer.

From these results we can deduce very easily the values of the integrals

$$\int_0^{\frac{\pi}{2}} \cos^n x\, dx, \int_0^{\frac{\pi}{2}} \sin^n x\, dx,$$

where n is a positive integer. We have

$$\int_0^{\frac{\pi}{2}} \cos^n x\, dx = \left[\frac{\sin x \cos^{n-1} x}{n}\right]_0^{\frac{\pi}{2}} + \frac{n-1}{n}\int_0^{\frac{\pi}{2}} \cos^{n-2} x\, dx$$

$$= \frac{n-1}{n}\int_0^{\frac{\pi}{2}} \cos^{n-2} x\, dx$$

$$= \frac{(n-1)\,(n-3)}{n(n-2)}\int_0^{\frac{\pi}{2}} \cos^{n-4} x\, dx, \text{ and so on.}$$

Continuing the process, we have finally, if n is odd,

$$\int_2^{\frac{\pi}{2}} \cos^n x\, dx = \frac{(n-1)\,(n-3)\,\ldots\,4\,.\,2}{n(n-2)\quad\ldots\,5\,.\,3}\int_0^{\frac{\pi}{2}} \cos x\, dx$$

$$= \frac{(n-1)\,(n-3)\,\ldots\,4\,.\,2}{n(n-2)\quad\ldots\,5\,.\,3},$$

and, if n is even,

$$\int_0^{\frac{\pi}{2}} \cos^n x\, dx = \frac{(n-1)(n-3)\,\ldots\,5\,.\,3}{n(n-2)\quad\ldots\,6\,.\,4}\int_0^{\frac{\pi}{2}} \cos^2 x\, dx$$

$$= \frac{(n-1)(n-3)\,\ldots\,5\,.\,3}{n(n-2)\quad\ldots\,4\,.\,2}\,.\,\frac{\pi}{2}.$$

Now by § 8

$$\int_0^{\frac{\pi}{2}} \sin^n x\, dx = \int_0^{\frac{\pi}{2}} \sin^n\left(\frac{\pi}{2}-x\right) dx = \int_0^{\frac{\pi}{2}} \cos^n x\, dx,$$

and thus the above formulæ hold for $\int_0^{\frac{\pi}{2}} \sin^n x\, dx$ as well as for $\int_0^{\frac{\pi}{2}} \cos^n x\, dx$.

(4) We shall now obtain a reduction formula for the integral of $\sin^m x \cos^n x$. Let

$$I\,(m, n) = \int \sin^m x \cos^n x\, dx = \int (\sin^m x \cos x)(\cos^{n-1} x)\, dx,$$

which gives, on integrating by parts,

$$I(m, n) = \frac{\sin^{m+1} x \cos^{n-1} x}{m+1} + \frac{n-1}{m+1}\int \sin^{m+2} x \cos^{n-2} x\, dx$$

$$= \frac{\sin^{m+1} x \cos^{n-1} x}{m+1} + \frac{n-1}{m+1} [I(m, n-2) - I(m, n)].$$

Hence we have the reduction formula

$$\int \sin^m x \cos^n x \, dx = \frac{\sin^{m+1} x \cos^{n-1} x}{m+n} + \frac{n-1}{m+n} \int \sin^m x \cos^{n-2} x \, dx,$$

which holds for all values of m and n for which the integrals exist.

We now use this formula to evaluate the definite integral $\int_0^{\frac{\pi}{2}} \sin^m x \cos^n x \, dx$, where m and n are positive integers.

If n is odd,

$$\int_0^{\frac{\pi}{2}} \sin^m x \cos^n x \, dx$$

$$= \left[\frac{\sin^{m+1} x \cos^{n-1} x}{m+n}\right]_0^{\frac{\pi}{2}} + \frac{n-1}{m+n} \int_0^{\frac{\pi}{2}} \sin^m x \cos^{n-2} x \, dx$$

$$= \frac{n-1}{m+n} \int_0^{\frac{\pi}{2}} \sin^m x \cos^{n-2} x \, dx$$

$$= \frac{(n-1)(n-3)}{(m+n)(m+n-2)} \int_0^{\frac{\pi}{2}} \sin^m x \cos^{n-4} x \, dx$$

$$= \frac{(n-1)(n-3) \quad \ldots \quad 4 \,.\, 2}{(m+n)(m+n-2) \ldots (m+5)(m+3)} \int_0^{\frac{\pi}{2}} \sin^m x \cos x \, dx$$

$$= \frac{(n-1)(n-3) \quad \ldots \quad 6 \,.\, 4 \,.\, 2}{(m+n)(m+n-2) \ldots (m+5)(m+3)(m+1)}.$$

(Note that in this case m need not be a positive integer.)

If n is even,

$$\int_0^{\frac{\pi}{2}} \sin^m x \cos^n x \, dx$$

$$= \frac{(n-1)(n-3) \quad \ldots \quad 3 \,.\, 1}{(m+n)(m+n-2) \ldots (m+4)(m+2)} \int_0^{\frac{\pi}{2}} \sin^m x \, dx$$

$$= \frac{(n-1)(n-3) \quad \dots \quad 3.1.(m-1)(m-3) \dots 3.1}{(m+n)(m+n-2) \dots (m+4)(m+2)m(m-2) \dots 4.2} \cdot \frac{\pi}{2},$$

when m is even, or

$$= \frac{(n-1)(n-3) \quad \dots \quad 3.1.(m-1)(m-3) \dots 4.2}{(m+n)(m+n-2) \dots (m+4)(m+2)m\,(m-2) \dots 3.1},$$

when m is odd.

Summing up, we have the final result

$$\int_0^{\frac{\pi}{2}} \sin^m x \cos^n x \, dx = \frac{(m-1)(m-3)\dots(n-1)(n-3)\dots}{(m+n)(m+n-2)\dots}\theta,$$

where $\theta = 1$, except when m and n are both even, in which case $\theta = \frac{\pi}{2}$.

It should be noted that the integrals $\int_0^{\frac{\pi}{2}} \cos^n x dx$ and $\int_0^{\frac{\pi}{2}} \sin^n x \, dx$ are special cases of this formula.

Ex. Show that

(i) $\int_0^{\frac{\pi}{2}} \sin^5 x \cos^4 x \, dx = \frac{8}{315}$, (ii) $\int_0^{\frac{\pi}{2}} \sin^4 x \cos^6 x \, dx = \frac{3\pi}{2^9}$.

If n is an odd integer, equal to $2k+1$, where k is an integer, positive or negative, the function $\sin^m x \cos^n x$ may be integrated by using the substitution $u = \sin x$. Then we obtain

$$\int \sin^m x \cos^n x \, dx = \int u^m(1-u^2)^k \, du,$$

in which the integrand is a rational function of u and so can be integrated. If m is odd, let $u = \cos x$.

If m, n are integers such that $m+n$ is a positive or negative even integer, let $u = \tan x$, and we have

$$\int \sin^m x \cos^n x \, dx = \int \frac{u^m}{(1+u^2)^{\frac{m+n}{2}+1}} \, du,$$

in which the integrand is rational.

(5) A rational function $f(\sin x, \cos x)$ of $\sin x$ and $\cos x$ can be integrated by means of the following important change of variable:

Let $t = \tan\dfrac{x}{2}$, so that $dt = \dfrac{1}{2}\sec^2\dfrac{x}{2}\,dx$, *i.e.*

$$\mathbf{dx = \frac{2dt}{1+t^2}, \ \sin x = \frac{2t}{1+t^2}, \ \cos x = \frac{1-t^2}{1+t^2}.}$$

Hence

$$\int f(\sin x, \cos x)\, dx = \int f\left(\frac{2t}{1+t^2}, \frac{1-t^2}{1+t^2}\right)\frac{2\,dt}{1+t^2},$$

in which the integrand is a rational function of t and so can be integrated. As an example, we have

$$\int \operatorname{cosec} x\, dx = \int \frac{1+t^2}{2t}\,\frac{2dt}{1+t^2} = \int \frac{dt}{t} = \log|\tan\tfrac{1}{2}x|,$$

and, by changing the variable to $x+\pi/2$, we deduce that

$$\int \sec x\, dx = \log\left|\tan\left(\frac{x}{2}+\frac{\pi}{4}\right)\right|.$$

In many cases the integration may be simplified by special substitutions; *e.g.* in

$$\int \frac{dx}{a\cos x + b\sin x}, \text{ let } u = x + \phi, \text{ where } \tan\phi = \frac{a}{b},$$

so that the integral is

$$\frac{1}{\sqrt{(a^2+b^2)}}\int \frac{du}{\sin u} = \frac{1}{\sqrt{(a^2+b^2)}}\log|\tan\tfrac{1}{2}(x+\phi)|.$$

(6) If the integrand is a rational function of $\sin^2 x$ and $\cos^2 x$, we may put $u = \tan x$, giving

$$dx = \frac{du}{1+u^2}, \quad \sin^2 x = \frac{u^2}{1+u^2}, \quad \cos^2 x = \frac{1}{1+u^2},$$

and the new integral is that of a rational function of u.

(7) An important and instructive example is the evaluation of $\int_0^{\frac{\pi}{2}} \log \sin x \, dx$. We have

$$\int_0^{\frac{\pi}{2}} \log \sin x \, dx = \int_0^{\frac{\pi}{2}} \log \sin \left(\frac{\pi}{2} - x\right) dx = \int_0^{\frac{\pi}{2}} \log \cos x \, dx$$

$$= \frac{1}{2}\int_0^{\frac{\pi}{2}} \log (\sin x \cos x) dx = \frac{1}{2}\int_0^{\frac{\pi}{2}} (\log \sin 2x - \log 2) \, dx$$

$$= \frac{1}{4}\int_0^{\pi} \log \sin x \, dx - \frac{\pi}{4} \log 2$$

$$= \frac{1}{2}\int_0^{\frac{\pi}{2}} \log \sin x \, dx - \frac{\pi}{4} \log 2,$$

and hence

$$\int_0^{\frac{\pi}{2}} \log \sin x \, dx = -\frac{\pi}{2} \log 2.$$

§ 12. Integration of Irrational Functions

It was shown in § 10 that a rational function can always be integrated in terms of the standard functions. In the case of irrational functions it is only very exceptionally that we can integrate in terms of known functions.

For example, the integral

$$\int_0^x \frac{dt}{\sqrt{\{(1-t^2)(1-k^2t^2)\}}}$$

cannot be expressed in terms of the standard functions, but may be used to define a new function.

In this paragraph we shall discuss certain irrational functions which can be integrated.

(1) *Rational function of x and* $\sqrt[n]{\left[\frac{a+bx}{p+qx}\right]}$, *where n is a positive integer.*

We can integrate this type of function by means of the

transformation $u^n = (a+bx)/(p+qx)$. For, we have

$$x = \frac{pu^n - a}{-qu^n + b},\ dx = n(pb-qa)\frac{u^{n-1}\,du}{(b-qu^n)^2},$$

and the integrand is now a rational function of u.

(2) *Rational function of x and $\sqrt{(ax^2+bx+c)}$.*

We can reduce the integration of this type of function to the integration of a rational function by means of the following methods:

(*a*) When the factors of ax^2+bx+c are real, *i.e.* when $b^2-4ac>0$, let $t = x+b/2a$, $k^2 = (b^2-4ac)/4a^2$; then

$$\sqrt{(ax^2+bx+c)} = \sqrt{\{a(t^2-k^2)\}} = (t+k)\sqrt{\left[\frac{at-ak}{t+k}\right]}.$$

The problem is now reduced to type (1).

(*b*) When the factors of ax^2+bx+c are not real, *i.e.* where $b^2-4ac<0$, we may assume that $a>0$, for otherwise $\sqrt{(ax^2+bx+c)}$ is not real for any value of x. Let $t = x+b/2a$, $k^2 = (4ac-b^2)/4a^2$, and thus $\sqrt{(ax^2+bx+c)} = \sqrt{a}\ \sqrt{(t^2+k^2)}$. Now let

$$u = t + \sqrt{(t^2+k^2)},$$

so that

$$t = \frac{u^2-k^2}{2u},\ dt = \frac{u^2+k^2}{2u^2}\,du,\ \sqrt{(t^2+k^2)} = \frac{u^2+k^2}{2u}.$$

It is clear that the integrand in u is a rational function.

(*c*) A method alternative to (*a*) of treating a rational function of x and $\sqrt{\{(x-\lambda_1)(\lambda_2-x)\}}$ is to let $x = \lambda_1 \cos^2\theta + \lambda_2 \sin^2\theta$, so that $dx = 2(\lambda_2-\lambda_1)\sin\theta\cos\theta\,d\theta$, and $\sqrt{\{(x-\lambda_1)(\lambda_2-x)\}} = (\lambda_2-\lambda_1)\sin\theta\cos\theta$.
The integrand is now a rational function of $\sin\theta$ and $\cos\theta$.

(3) The function

$$\frac{ex+f}{(ax^2+bx+c)\sqrt{(a'x^2+b'x+c')}}$$

could of course be integrated as above since it is of type (2), but it is easier to use the following substitution, called a homographic transformation. Let $x = (\lambda t+\mu)/(t+1)$, where λ, μ are constants to be determined; then

$$ax^2+bx+c = \frac{t^2(a\lambda^2+b\lambda+c)+t[2a\lambda\mu+b(\lambda+\mu)+2c]+a\mu^2+b\mu+c}{(t+1)^2},$$

$$a'x^2+b'x+c' = \frac{t^2(a'\lambda^2+b'\lambda+c')+t[2a'\lambda\mu+b'(\lambda+\mu)+2c']+a'\mu^2+b'\mu+c'}{(t+1)^2}.$$

If we can choose λ, μ so that

$$2a\lambda\mu+b(\lambda+\mu)+2c = 0,$$
$$2a'\lambda\mu+b'(\lambda+\mu)+2c' = 0,$$

it is easy to see that the integral is now of the form

$$\int \frac{lt+m}{(pt^2+q)\sqrt{(rt^2+s)}}\,dt = l\int\frac{du}{pu^2+(qr-ps)} - m\int\frac{dv}{qv^2+(ps-qr)},$$

where $u^2 = rt^2+s$, $v^2 = r+s/t^2$.

Ex. Evaluate the integrals

(i) $\displaystyle\int_1^3 \frac{dx}{(x^2-2x+5)\sqrt{(x^2-4x+7)}}$,

(ii) $\displaystyle\int_0^1 \frac{(1-x)dx}{(x^2+1)\sqrt{(x^2-x+1)}}$.

[Ans.: (i) $\dfrac{1}{4}\left\{\dfrac{1}{2\sqrt{2}}\log(3+2\sqrt{2})+\dfrac{1}{\sqrt{2}}\tan^{-1}\dfrac{1}{2\sqrt{2}}\right\}$,

(ii) $\sqrt{2}\tan^{-1}\dfrac{1}{2\sqrt{2}}$.]

Examples I

1. Integrate the functions

(i) $x\sec^2 x$, (ii) $\dfrac{x+1}{\sqrt{(3x+2)}}$, (iii) $\dfrac{1}{x(x^2+1)^2}$,

(iv) $\dfrac{1}{x\sqrt{\{(1+x)(2-x)\}}}$, (v) $\dfrac{1}{a+b\tan x}$,

(vi) $x(1-x^{2/3})^{\frac{1}{3}}$, (vii) $\sqrt{\left(\dfrac{x+2}{x+4}\right)}$.

2. Sketch the curve $a(x^2-y^2) = x^3$, and find the area of the loop.

3. Sketch the curve $(1+x)y^2 = 1-x$, and evaluate

(i) the area between the curve and its asymptote ;

(ii) the volume generated by revolving about the x-axis the area bounded by the curve and the y-axis and lying to the right of the y-axis.

4. Show that

$$\int \sin^{n-1} x \sin (n+1)x\, dx = \frac{1}{n} \sin^n x \sin nx.$$

5. Evaluate the integrals

(i) $\displaystyle\int_0^{\pi} x \log \sin x\, dx$, (ii) $\displaystyle\int_0^{\frac{\pi}{2}} \frac{\sin 2x}{\sqrt{(1-k\sin x)}}\, dx$, where $k<1$,

(iii) $\displaystyle\int_0^{\frac{\pi}{2}} \log \frac{1+\sin x}{1+\cos x}\, dx$, (iv) $\displaystyle\int_0^{\frac{\pi}{4}} \log (1+\tan x)\, dx$.

6. Prove that

$$\int \cos^m x \cos nx\, dx = \frac{1}{m+n} \cos^m x \sin nx + \frac{m}{m+n} \int \cos^{m-1} x \cos (n-1)x\, dx.$$

7. If $I_n = \int (a+b\cos\theta)^{-n} d\theta$, establish the reduction formula

$$(n-1)(a^2-b^2)I_n = (2n-3)aI_{n-1}-(n-2)I_{n-2}-b\sin\theta\,(a+b\cos\theta)^{-n+1},$$

and evaluate the integral

$$\int_0^{\pi} (5+3\cos\theta)^{-3}\, d\theta.$$

8. If $I_n = \int e^{px} (\sin qx)^n\, dx$, show that

$$I_n = \frac{e^{px}(\sin qx)^{n-1}\sin(qx-\phi)}{\sqrt{(p^2+n^2q^2)}} + \frac{n(n-1)q^2}{p^2+n^2q^2}I_{n-2},$$

where $\tan\phi = nq/p$.

9. Integrate the functions

(i) $\dfrac{x^3-x^2-1}{(x^2+1)^2(x^2+x+1)}$, (ii) $\dfrac{2x-3}{(2x^2-6x+5)\sqrt{(5x^2-12x+8)}}$.

10. Evaluate the integrals

(i) $\displaystyle\int_0^1 \frac{dx}{x+1+\sqrt{(x^2+1)}}$, (ii) $\displaystyle\int_0^\infty \frac{dx}{\{x+\sqrt{(x^2+a^2)}\}^n}$,

where $n>1$, $a>0$.

11. Employ the substitution $x+1/x = 1/u$ to find the integral of

$$\frac{x^2-1}{x^2+1}\,\frac{1}{\sqrt{(x^4+4px^3+4x^2+4px+1)}}.$$

12. If n is a positive integer and $m>-1$, show that

$$\int_0^1 x^m(\log x)^n dx = (-1)^n\frac{n!}{(m+1)^{n+1}}.$$

13. Evaluate the integrals

(i) $\displaystyle\int_1^2 \frac{dx}{(1+x)\sqrt{(1+x+x^2)}}$, (ii) $\displaystyle\int_1^3 \frac{x^2+6x-25}{(x^2-4x)^2-25}\,dx$.

14. Show that the integral of

$$\frac{Ax^2+2Hx+B}{\sqrt{\{(x-a)^2+b^2\}}}$$

will be algebraic (*i.e.* free from logarithms) provided

$$(a^2-\tfrac{1}{2}b^2)A+2aH+B = 0.$$

15. Prove that

$$\int_0^{\frac{\pi}{2}} \frac{\sin 2nx}{\sin x}\,dx = 2\left[1-\frac{1}{3}+\frac{1}{5}-\ldots+(-1)^{n-1}\frac{1}{2n-1}\right],$$

where n is a positive integer.

16. Integrate the function

$$\frac{\sin x}{\sin (x-a) \sin (x-b) \sin (x-c)}.$$

17. If $I_n = \int (1+ax^2)^n dx$, show that

$$(2n+1)I_n - 2nI_{n-1} = x(1+ax^2)^n.$$

18. Evaluate the integrals

$$\text{(i)} \int_0^1 \tan^{-1}x \, dx, \qquad \text{(ii)} \int_1^4 \frac{x\,dx}{\sqrt{(-x^2+5x-4)}}.$$

19. If n is a positive integer, show that

$$\int_0^{2a} (2ax-x^2)^{n-\frac{1}{2}} \cos^{-1}\left(1-\frac{x}{a}\right) dx = \frac{\pi^2 a^{2n} \,.\, 2n!}{2^{2n+1}(n!)^2}.$$

20. If $ac-b^2>0$, and n is a positive integer, prove that

$$\int_{-\infty}^{\infty} \frac{dx}{(ax^2+2bx+c)^n} = \pi \frac{(2n-2)!}{2^{2n-2}[(n-1)!]^2} \frac{a^{n-1}}{(ac-b^2)^{n-\frac{1}{2}}}.$$

[Answers: 2. $8a^2/15$; 3. (i) 2π, (ii) $\pi(2\log 2-1)$; 5. (i) $-\frac{\pi^2}{2}\log 2$, (ii) $4\{2-(2+k)\sqrt{(1-k)}\}/3k^2$, (iii) 0, (iv) $\frac{\pi}{8}\log 2$; 7. $\frac{59\pi}{2^{11}}$; 10. (i) $\frac{1}{2}\left\{\log\frac{1+\sqrt{2}}{2}+(2-\sqrt{2})\right\}$, (ii) $\frac{n}{n^2-1}\frac{1}{a^{n-1}}$; 13. (i) $\log\frac{\sqrt{3}(1+2\sqrt{7})}{9}$, (ii) $\frac{\pi}{2}$; 18. (i) $\frac{\pi}{4}-\frac{1}{2}\log 2$. (ii) $\frac{5\pi}{2}$.]

CHAPTER III

MULTIPLE INTEGRALS

§ 13. Double Integrals

WE saw in Chapter I that an area can be expressed as a definite integral, and we now proceed to apply a similar limiting process to the problem of evaluating the volume of a solid figure.

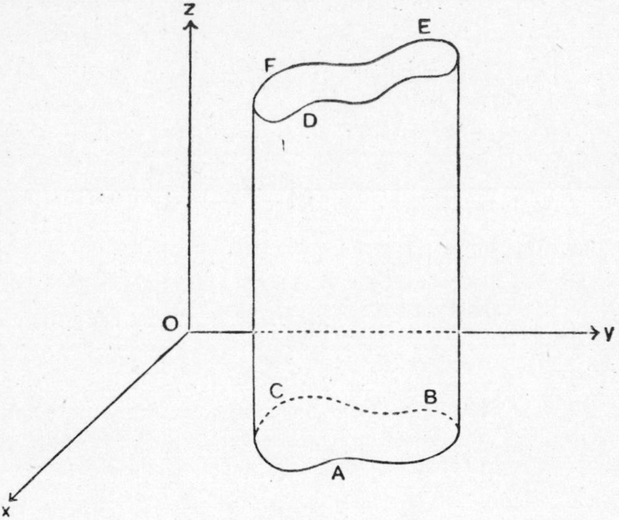

FIG. 3.

Let ABC be a closed curve in the plane XOY, and let $z = f(x,y)$ be the equation of a surface, $f(x,y)$ being single-valued, so that any line parallel to OZ meets the surface in only one point. To begin with we shall take $f(x,y)$ to be positive. The cylinder generated by lines parallel to OZ passing through the curve ABC meets the surface $z = f(x, y)$ in the curve DEF. The volume we wish to evaluate is that of the solid figure bounded by the plane $z = 0$, the cylinder on ABC and the portion DEF of the surface cut off by the cylinder.

In the plane $z = 0$ let the curve ABC be wholly enclosed within a rectangle whose sides are parallel to the x and y axes and have equations $x = a$, $x = b$, $y = c$, $y = d$, where $a<b$, $c<d$.

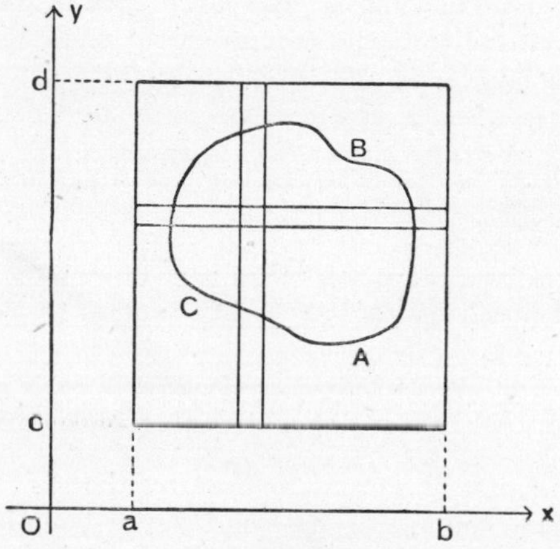

FIG. 4.

The rectangle is now divided into mn small rectangles by lines $x = x_r$, where $r = 0, 1, 2, \ldots, m$, and $y = y_s$, where $s = 0, 1, 2, \ldots, n$, and

$$a = x_0<x_1<x_2< \ldots <x_m = b,$$
$$c = y_0<y_1<y_2< \ldots <y_n = d.$$

In each of the mn rectangles any point is taken; the typical point being (ξ_{rs}, η_{rs}) in the rectangle whose sides are $x = x_{r-1}$, $x = x_r$, $y = y_{s-1}$, $y = y_s$. We now define the function $F(x, y)$ as equal to $f(x, y)$ for all points inside and on the curve ABC and equal to zero for all points of the rectangle outside the curve ABC. The expression

$$F(\xi_{rs}, \eta_{rs})(x_r-x_{r-1})(y_s-y_{s-1})$$

is the volume of the cuboid on the small rectangle as base and of height $F(\xi_{rs}, \eta_{rs})$. If we sum all such expressions over all the small rectangles we have a sum of volumes of cuboids which is approximately equal to the volume of the solid figure we wish to measure. As m and n grow larger in such a way that each small rectangle becomes smaller in area, this sum becomes more nearly equal to the required volume. We say that the volume of the solid figure is the limit of this sum as m and n tend to infinity in such a way that the area of each small rectangle tends to zero. This limit

$$\lim_{\substack{m\to\infty \\ n\to\infty}} \sum_{\substack{r=1,m \\ s=1,n}} F(\xi_{rs}, \eta_{rs})(x_r-x_{r-1})(y_s-y_{s-1})$$

is called the **double integral** of the function $f(x, y)$ over the area enclosed by the curve ABC and is written

$$\iint_{\mathbf{K}} \mathbf{f(x, y)\, dx\, dy},$$

where K denotes the area enclosed by the curve ABC. It measures the volume of the solid figure bounded by the plane $z = 0$, the surface $z = f(x, y)$ and the cylinder formed by lines parallel to the z-axis passing through the curve ABC in the plane $z = 0$. The area over which we integrate in the plane $z = 0$, *i.e.* the area enclosed by the curve ABC, is called the **field of integration.**

As an example let us take the octant of the sphere $x^2+y^2+z^2 = a^2$ for which x, y, z are all positive. The volume of this octant is clearly

$$\iint \sqrt{(a^2-x^2-y^2)}\, dxdy,$$

taken over the part of the circle $x^2+y^2 = a^2$ which lies in the first quadrant. Since it can be shown that the volume of the sphere is $4\pi a^3/3$, the value of this double integral is $\pi a^3/6$.

If $f(x, y) \equiv 1$, the double integral $\iint_K dx\,dy$ is the volume of the cylinder of uniform height one unit erected on the area K and is therefore a measure of the area K enclosed by the curve ABC.

If $f(x, y)$ is negative, *i.e.* if the surface lies below the plane $z = 0$, the double integral is obviously negative. Hence, if we make the convention that volumes lying below the plane $z = 0$ have negative sign, the double integral measures the volume in all cases.

§ 14. Repeated Integrals

The above discussion gives no practical method of carrying out the actual integration. In this section we shall show that the integration can be performed in two stages, each stage being an ordinary integration of the type discussed in Chapter I.

We assume that any line parallel to the x or y axes meets the curve ABC in at most two points. If this is not so, we can divide the area into portions for which this is the case and perform the integration for each of these portions.

Let us choose the smallest rectangle (Fig. 5) with sides parallel to the axes ($x = a, b$; $y = c, d$) which encloses the area, and divide the rectangle into small rectangles as in the last paragraph. We now form the sum

$$\Sigma\, F(\xi_{rs}, \eta_{rs})(x_r - x_{r-1})(y_s - y_{s-1})$$

as before, but this time we perform the summation in a certain order. Let r have a fixed value and let us make the sum from $s = 1$ to $s = n$. We thus obtain the sum of all the cuboids lying between the planes $x = x_{r-1}$, $x = x_r$.

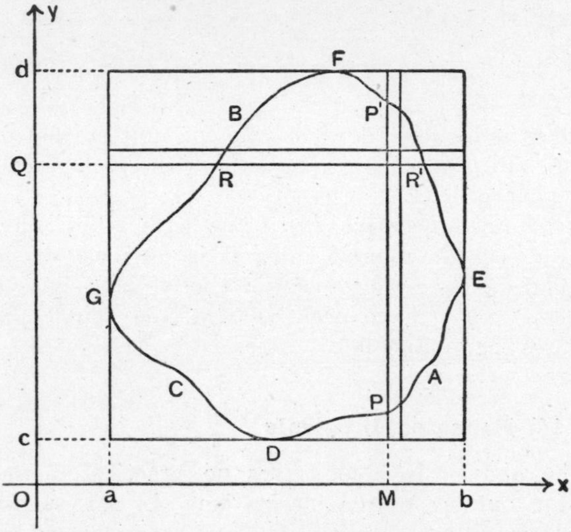

FIG. 5.

For sufficiently large values of m and n this is approximately the volume of the part of the solid figure lying between these planes. This sum is approximately

$$(x_r - x_{r-1}) \sum_{s=1}^{n} F(x_r, \eta_{rs})(y_s - y_{s-1})$$

and the limit of this sum for n tending to infinity is, by § 3,

$$(x_r - x_{r-1}) \int_c^d F(x_r, y)dy,$$

which, from the definition of $F(x, y)$, is equal to

$$(x_r - x_{r-1}) \int_{MP}^{MP'} f(x_r, y)dy.$$

In this integration x_r is kept constant. Let GDE, the lower portion of the curve ABC, have the equation $y = \phi_1(x)$, and let GFE have the equation $y = \phi_2(x)$; hence $MP = \phi_1(x_r)$, $MP' = \phi_2(x_r)$. It follows that the integral

$$\int_{MP}^{MP'} f(x_r, y)dy \text{ is a function of } x_r, \ \phi(x_r) \text{ say.}$$

We now complete the summation by letting r take the values 1 to m, and thus we obtain

$$\sum_{r=1}^{m} \phi(x_r)(x_r - x_{r-1}).$$

The limit of this sum when m tends to infinity so that each $(x_r - x_{r-1})$ tends to zero is $\int_a^b \phi(x)dx$, where

$$\phi(x) = \int_{\phi_1(x)}^{\phi_2(x)} f(x, y)dy.$$

Hence the required volume is

$$\int_a^b \left[\int_{\phi_1(x)}^{\phi_2(x)} f(x, y)dy\right]dx,$$

where in the inner integral x is kept constant during integration. This type of integral is called a **repeated integral** and is written

$$\int_a^b dx \int_{\phi_1(x)}^{\phi_2(x)} f(x, y)dy \quad \text{or} \quad \int_a^b \int_{\phi_1(x)}^{\phi_2(x)} f(x, y)dx\, dy.$$

We now change the order in which we perform the summation and obtain the volume as another repeated integral. We begin by letting s have a fixed value and we obtain the sum of the volumes of the cuboids lying between the planes $y = y_{s-1}$ and $y = y_s$. Proceeding as before, we obtain

$$\int_c^d \left[\int_{QR}^{QR'} f(x, y)dx\right]dy\,;$$

and if $x = \psi_1(y)$, $x = \psi_2(y)$ are the equations of the curves *FGD*, *FED* respectively, the volume is given by

$$\int_c^d dy \int_{\psi_1(y)}^{\psi_2(y)} f(x, y)dx.$$

In the inner integral in this case y is kept constant. Since we have expressed the volume of the solid figure as repeated integrals, these two repeated integrals must be equal and equal to the double integral ; *i.e.*

$$\iint_{\mathbf{K}} \mathbf{f(x, y)dx\,dy} = \int_{\mathbf{a}}^{\mathbf{b}} \mathbf{dx} \int_{\phi_1(\mathbf{x})}^{\phi_2(\mathbf{x})} \mathbf{f(x, y)dy} = \int_{\mathbf{c}}^{\mathbf{d}} \mathbf{dy} \int_{\psi_1(\mathbf{y})}^{\psi_2(\mathbf{y})} \mathbf{f(x, y)dx}.$$

The process will be made clear by means of the following examples. It is important that the student should work through them very carefully.

Ex. 1. To find the volume of the sphere of radius a.

We shall calculate the volume of the octant of the sphere $x^2+y^2+z^2 = a^2$ in which x, y, z are positive. We saw that this volume is the double integral $\iint \sqrt{(a^2-x^2-y^2)}dx\,dy$ over the first quadrant of the circle $x^2+y^2 = a^2$.

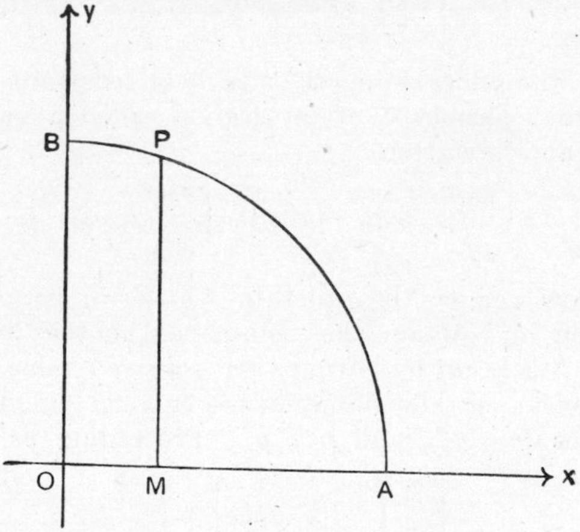

FIG. 6.

This double integral can be expressed as the repeated integral

$$\int_0^a dx \int_0^{MP} \sqrt{(a^2-x^2-y^2)}dy,$$

where M is the point on the x-axis of abscissa x. Now $MP = \sqrt{(a^2-x^2)}$, so that the inner integral is

$$\int_0^{\sqrt{(a^2-x^2)}} \sqrt{(a^2-x^2-y^2)}dy.$$

Performing this integration and remembering that x is to be kept constant, we obtain

$$\left[\frac{y}{2}\sqrt{(a^2-x^2-y^2)}+\frac{a^2-x^2}{2}\sin^{-1}\frac{y}{\sqrt{(a^2-x^2)}}\right]_0^{\sqrt{(a^2-x^2)}}$$

$$= \frac{\pi}{4}(a^2-x^2).$$

The double integral is now

$$\frac{\pi}{4}\int_0^a (a^2-x^2)dx = \frac{\pi}{6}a^3.$$

Thus the volume of the sphere is $8\dfrac{\pi a^3}{6} = \dfrac{4\pi a^3}{3}$.

Ex. 2. Change the order of integration in the repeated integral

$$\int_0^3 dx \int_{\frac{4x}{3}}^{\sqrt{(25-x^2)}} f(x, y)dy.$$

The first step in tackling a problem of this kind is to make a sketch of the field of integration.

In this case the field is the area in the first quadrant bounded by the circle $x^2+y^2 = 25$ and the lines $x = 0$, $3y = 4x$. Between $y = 0$ and $y = 4$ a line parallel to the x-axis meets the boundary of the field in $x = 0$ and $x = 3y/4$, while between $y = 4$ and $y = 5$ a line parallel to the x-axis meets the boundary in $x = 0$ and $x = \sqrt{(25-y^2)}$. Therefore,

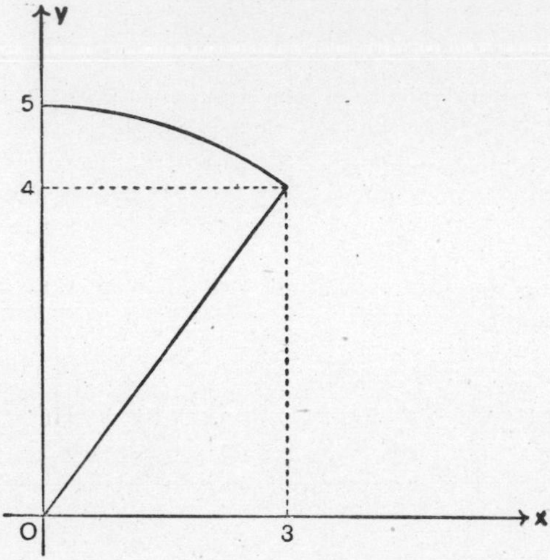

FIG. 7.

when the order is changed, the field has to be divided into two parts and the integral is

$$\int_0^4 dy \int_0^{3y/4} f(x, y)dx + \int_4^5 dy \int_0^{\sqrt{(25-y^2)}} f(x, y)dx.$$

If the field of integration is a rectangle with sides $x = a$, $x = b$, $y = c$, $y = d$, the double integral of the function $f(x, y)$ over this field can be expressed as

$$\int_a^b dx \int_c^d f(x, y)dy \text{ or as} \int_c^d dy \int_a^b f(x, y)dx.$$

In this case, and in this case only, the limits of integration for x and y are the same for both the orders of integration. If, further, $f(x, y)$ can be expressed as the product of a function of x and a function of y, the double integral is simply the product of two definite integrals; *e.g.* if $f(x, y) \equiv \phi(x)\psi(y)$,

$$\iint f(x, y)dx\,dy = \int_a^b \phi(x)dx \times \int_c^d \psi(y)dy.$$

§ 15. Triple Integrals

It is easy to extend the process of double integration to that of triple integration. In this case the function to be integrated is $f(x, y, z)$, a function of the three variables x, y, z, and the "field" of integration is now a closed volume A in three-dimensional space. We enclose this volume in a parallelepiped whose faces have the equations $x = a, b$; $y = c, d$; $z = e, f$. This parallelepiped is divided into lmn small parallelepipeds by planes $x = x_r$, $y = y_s$, $z = z_t$, where $r = 0, 1, \ldots, l$; $s = 0, 1, \ldots, m$; $t = 0, 1, \ldots, n$; $x_0 = a$, $x_l = b$, $y_0 = c$, $y_m = d$, $z_0 = e$, $z_n = f$. In each small volume we take any point, $(\xi_{rst}, \eta_{rst}, \zeta_{rst})$ being the typical one, and we form the sum

$$\Sigma F(\xi_{rst}, \eta_{rst}, \zeta_{rst})(x_r - x_{r-1})(y_s - y_{s-1})(z_t - z_{t-1})$$

over all the lmn small volumes, where $F(x, y, z)$ is the function which is equal to $f(x, y, z)$ inside A and equal to zero outside A. The limit of this sum as l, m, n tend to infinity so that each small volume tends to zero is called the **triple integral** of $f(x, y, z)$ throughout the given volume. This is written

$$\iiint_A \mathbf{f(x, y, z)dx\,dy\,dz}.$$

If $f(x, y, z) \equiv 1$, the triple integral measures the volume of the space A.

Exactly as in the case of the double integral this triple integral can be expressed as a repeated integral; for example, as

$$\int_a^b dx \int_{\phi_1(x)}^{\phi_2(x)} dy \int_{\psi_1(x, y)}^{\psi_2(x, y)} f(x, y, z)dz.$$

There are six ways in which we can express the triple integral as a repeated integral, according to the order in which we integrate with respect to the variables x, y and z. The manner in which the limits of integration a, b, $\phi_1(x)$, $\phi_2(x)$, $\psi_1(x, y)$, $\psi_2(x, y)$ are obtained is best seen by taking an example. Let us evaluate the triple integral of the function $1/(x+y+z+1)^3$ throughout the volume bounded by the coordinate planes and the plane $x+y+z = 1$.

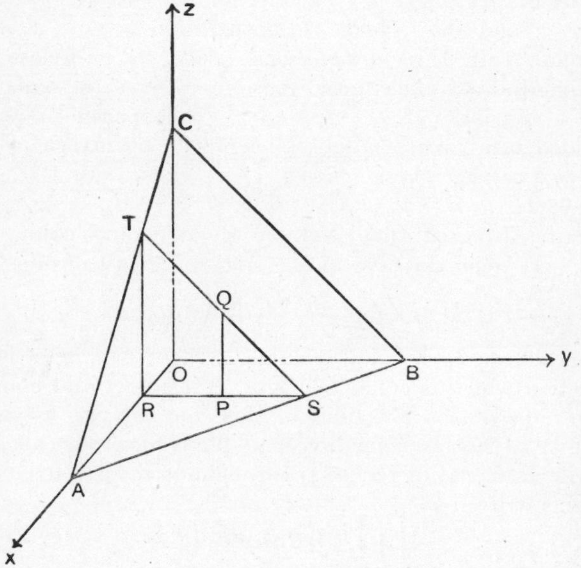

FIG. 8.

We shall integrate first with regard to z, then with regard to y, and finally with regard to x. Take a line parallel to the z-axis through the point $P(x, y, 0)$, meeting the plane $x+y+z = 1$ in $Q(x, y, 1-x-y)$. Thus the limits of integration with respect to z are 0 and $1-x-y$. In the next integral x is kept constant and the limits of integration are y_R and y_S, *i.e.* 0 and $1-x$; and in the final integral the limits of integration are 0 and x_A, *i.e.* 0 and 1. The first integral gives the integral of the function along the line *PQ*, the first two integrals together give the double integral of the function over the triangle *RST* and the final result is the triple integral of the function throughout the tetrahedron *OABC*. We shall now perform the integration:

$$\int_0^1 dx \int_0^{1-x} dy \int_0^{1-x-y} \frac{dz}{(1+x+y+z)^3}$$

$$= \int_0^1 dx \int_0^{1-x} \left[\frac{1}{2(x+y+1)^2} - \frac{1}{2^3}\right] dy$$

$$= \int_0^1 \left[\frac{1}{2(x+1)} - \frac{1}{4} - \frac{1-x}{8}\right] dx = \frac{1}{2}\left(\log 2 - \frac{5}{8}\right).$$

Ex. Evaluate $\iiint (ax+by+cz)^2 dx\, dy\, dz$ throughout the sphere $x^2+y^2+z^2=1$.

This is an important type of example. The perpendicular distance p of the point (x, y, z) from the plane $ax+by+cz=0$ is given by $|ax+by+cz|/\sqrt{(a^2+b^2+c^2)}$. Thus the given integral is

$$(a^2+b^2+c^2)\iiint p^2\, dx\, dy\, dz.$$

Now from the symmetry of the sphere this is equal to

$$(a^2+b^2+c^2)\iiint z^2 dx\, dy\, dz$$

$$= 8(a^2+b^2+c^2)\int_0^1 dx \int_0^{\sqrt{(1-x^2)}} dy \int_0^{\sqrt{(1-x^2-y^2)}} z^2\, dz$$

$$= \frac{8}{3}(a^2+b^2+c^2)\int_0^1 dx \int_0^{\sqrt{(1-x^2)}} (1-x^2-y^2)^{3/2} dy$$

$$= \frac{\pi}{2}(a^2+b^2+c^2)\int_0^1 (1-x^2)^2 dx = \frac{4\pi}{15}(a^2+b^2+c^2).$$

§ 16. Change of Variable in Multiple Integrals

Let us consider the double integral

$$\iint_A f(x, y)\, dx\, dy$$

taken over the area A in the (x, y) plane, and let us introduce new variables u, v defined by the relations

$$x = f_1(u, v)\ ,\ y = f_2(u, v). \quad . \quad . \quad . \quad (1)$$

The problem is to express the double integral as a double integral with respect to the new variables. We shall assume that the equations (1) can be solved for u and v in terms of x and y. This means that to each point in the (u, v) plane there corresponds a point in the (x, y) plane, and to each point in the (x, y) plane there corresponds a point in the (u, v) plane. Hence there is an area A' in the (u, v) plane which corresponds to the area A in the (x, y) plane.

Let us suppose that the area A' is divided into small portions by sets of straight lines parallel to the u, v axes. These lines correspond to sets of curves in the (x, y) plane dividing the area A into small portions. Let ΔS represent a typical small portion of A, and let (x, y) be any point of ΔS. The sum

$$\Sigma f(x, y)\Delta S,$$

taken over all the small portions of A, gives, just as in § 13, a sum of volumes which is approximately the volume of the solid figure standing on A and bounded by the surface $z = f(x, y)$. Thus

$$\iint_A f(x, y) dx\, dy = \lim \Sigma f(x, y)\Delta S,$$

as the number of small portions tends to infinity, each small area tending to zero.

Each small area corresponds to a small area in the (u, v) plane. Let ΔS correspond to the rectangle whose vertices are

$$(u, v), (u+\Delta u, v), (u+\Delta u, v+\Delta v), (u, v+\Delta v),$$

so that the vertices of ΔS are

$$[f_1(u, v), f_2(u, v)], [f_1(u+\Delta u, v), f_2(u+\Delta u, v)],$$
$$[f_1(u+\Delta u, v+\Delta v), f_2(u+\Delta u, v+\Delta v)],$$
$$[f_1(u, v+\Delta v), f_2(u, v+\Delta v)].$$

Now by Taylor's Theorem

$f_1(u+\Delta u, v) = f_1(u, v)+\dfrac{\partial f_1}{\partial u}\Delta u+$terms involving higher powers of Δu,

$f_1(u+\Delta u, v+\Delta v) = f_1(u, v)+\dfrac{\partial f_1}{\partial u}\Delta u+\dfrac{\partial f_1}{\partial v}\Delta v+$ terms involving higher powers of Δu and Δv,

and similarly for the others. Thus, when Δu and Δv are very small, the vertices of ΔS are approximately

$$(x, y), \left(x+\frac{\partial x}{\partial u}\Delta u, y+\frac{\partial y}{\partial u}\Delta u\right),$$

$$\left(x+\frac{\partial x}{\partial u}\Delta u+\frac{\partial x}{\partial v}\Delta v, y+\frac{\partial y}{\partial u}\Delta u+\frac{\partial y}{\partial v}\Delta v\right), \left(x+\frac{\partial x}{\partial v}\Delta v, y+\frac{\partial y}{\partial v}\Delta v\right).$$

Again, when Δu, Δv are very small, the area of ΔS is approximately the area of the rectangle with these vertices. This area is twice the area of the triangle whose vertices are

$$(x\ y), \left(x+\frac{\partial x}{\partial u}\Delta u, y+\frac{\partial y}{\partial u}\Delta u\right), \left(x+\frac{\partial x}{\partial v}\Delta v, y+\frac{\partial y}{\partial v}\Delta v\right);$$

i.e. the area of ΔS is approximately the numerical value of

$$2\times\frac{1}{2}\begin{vmatrix} 1 & 1 & 1 \\ x & x+\frac{\partial x}{\partial u}\Delta u & x+\frac{\partial x}{\partial v}\Delta v \\ y & y+\frac{\partial y}{\partial u}\Delta u & y+\frac{\partial y}{\partial v}\Delta v \end{vmatrix} = \begin{vmatrix} 1 & 0 & 0 \\ x & \frac{\partial x}{\partial u}\Delta u & \frac{\partial x}{\partial v}\Delta v \\ y & \frac{\partial y}{\partial u}\Delta u & \frac{\partial y}{\partial v}\Delta v \end{vmatrix}$$

$$= \begin{vmatrix} \frac{\partial x}{\partial u} & \frac{\partial x}{\partial v} \\ \frac{\partial y}{\partial u} & \frac{\partial y}{\partial v} \end{vmatrix} \Delta u \Delta v = \frac{\partial(x, y)}{\partial(u, v)} \Delta u \Delta v,$$

where $\frac{\partial(x, y)}{\partial(u, v)}$ is called **the Jacobian** * of (x, y) with respect to (u, v).

Hence

$$\Sigma f(x, y)\Delta S = \Sigma F(u, v) \left| \frac{\partial(x, y)}{\partial(u, v)} \right| \Delta u \Delta v + \epsilon,$$

where $F(u, v) = f[x(u, v), y(u, v)]$, $\epsilon \to 0$ as each $\Delta u, \Delta v \to 0$, and the second summation is over all the small rectangles in A'. Thus

$$\iint_A f(x, y)dx\, dy = \lim \Sigma f(x, y)\Delta S$$

$$= \lim \Sigma F(u, v) \left| \frac{\partial(x, y)}{\partial(u, v)} \right| \Delta u \Delta v$$

$$= \iint_{A'} F(u, v) \left| \frac{\partial(x, y)}{\partial(u, v)} \right| du\, dv.$$

To illustrate the method let us take the integral

$$\iint_A xy\, dx\, dy$$

where A is the area enclosed by the four parabolas

* Aitken, *Determinants and Matrices*, p. 128.

$y^2 = x$, $y^2 = 2x$, $x^2 = y$, $x^2 = 2y$. Let $u = y^2/x$, $v = x^2/y$, so that

$$xy = uv, \qquad \frac{\partial(x, y)}{\partial(u, v)} = -\frac{1}{3}$$

and the area A' in the (u, v) plane is the square bounded by the lines $u = 1, 2$, $v = 1, 2$. The integral is therefore

$$\frac{1}{3}\int_1^2 u\,du \int_1^2 v\,dv = \frac{3}{4}.$$

Similarly we can transform the triple integral

$$\iiint\limits_K f(x, y, z)dx\,dy\,dz,$$

taken throughout the volume K in (x, y, z) space, by means of the equations

$$x = f_1(u, v, w),\ y = f_2(u, v, w),\ z = f_3(u, v, w).$$

These equations define a volume K' in the (u, v, w) space, which corresponds to K. We now divide K' into small portions by sets of planes parallel to $u = 0$, $v = 0$, $w = 0$. These small portions correspond to small portions ΔV of K cut off by the surfaces corresponding to the planes which divide up K'. Let ΔV correspond to the parallelepiped whose vertices are (u, v, w), $(u+\Delta u, v, w)$, $(u, v+\Delta v, w)$, $(u, v, w+\Delta w)$, etc. Then, as above, the vertices of ΔV

are approximately (x, y, z), $\left(x+\frac{\partial x}{\partial u}\Delta u,\ y+\frac{\partial y}{\partial u}\Delta u,\ z+\frac{\partial z}{\partial u}\Delta u\right)$,

$$\left(x+\frac{\partial x}{\partial v}\Delta v, y+\frac{\partial y}{\partial v}\Delta v, z+\frac{\partial z}{\partial v}\Delta v\right), \left(x+\frac{\partial x}{\partial w}\Delta w, y+\frac{\partial y}{\partial w}\Delta w, z+\frac{\partial z}{\partial w}\Delta w\right),$$

etc. Hence the volume of ΔV is approximately the

numerical value of

$$6\times\frac{1}{6}\begin{vmatrix} 1 & 1 & 1 & 1 \\ x & x+\frac{\partial x}{\partial u}\Delta u & x+\frac{\partial x}{\partial v}\Delta v & x+\frac{\partial x}{\partial w}\Delta w \\ y & y+\frac{\partial y}{\partial u}\Delta u & y+\frac{\partial y}{\partial v}\Delta v & y+\frac{\partial y}{\partial w}\Delta w \\ z & z+\frac{\partial z}{\partial u}\Delta u & z+\frac{\partial z}{\partial v}\Delta v & z+\frac{\partial z}{\partial w}\Delta w \end{vmatrix}$$

$$= \begin{vmatrix} 1 & 0 & 0 & 0 \\ x & \frac{\partial x}{\partial u}\Delta u & \frac{\partial x}{\partial v}\Delta v & \frac{\partial x}{\partial w}\Delta w \\ y & \frac{\partial y}{\partial u}\Delta u & \frac{\partial y}{\partial v}\Delta v & \frac{\partial y}{\partial w}\Delta w \\ z & \frac{\partial z}{\partial u}\Delta u & \frac{\partial z}{\partial v}\Delta v & \frac{\partial z}{\partial w}\Delta w \end{vmatrix} = \frac{\partial(x, y, z)}{\partial(u, v, w)}\Delta u\Delta v\Delta w,$$

where $\dfrac{\partial(x, y, z)}{\partial(u, v, w)}$ is the Jacobian of (x, y, z) with respect to (u, v, w). Thus

$$\iiint_K f(x, y, z)dx\,dy\,dz = \iiint_{K'} F(u, v, w)\left|\frac{\partial(x, y, z)}{\partial(u,v, w)}\right| du\,dv\,dw,$$

where $F(u, v, w) = f[x(u, v, w), y(u, v, w), z(u, v, w)]$.

§ 17. Polar Coordinates

A very important application of the method of the last paragraph is the transformation of double and triple integrals into integrals with respect to r, θ and r, θ, ϕ, polar and spherical polar coordinates. In the case of the double integral

$$x = r\cos\theta,\ y = r\sin\theta,$$

so that

$$\frac{\partial(x, y)}{\partial(r, \theta)} = \begin{vmatrix} \cos\theta & \sin\theta \\ -r\sin\theta & r\cos\theta \end{vmatrix} = r.$$

Hence

$$\iint f(x,y)dxdy = \iint F(r,\theta)rd\theta dr,$$

where $$F(r,\ \theta) = f[r\cos\theta,\ r\sin\theta].$$

If $F(r,\ \theta)\equiv 1$, the double integral $\iint r\,d\theta\,dr$ is a measure of the area of the field of integration. When the field is the area bounded by the curve whose polar equation is $r = f(\theta)$, and the radii vectores $\theta = \alpha$, $\theta = \beta$, the double integral expression for the area reduces to a single integral with respect to θ. The area is given by

$$\int_{\alpha}^{\beta} d\theta \int_{0}^{f(\theta)} r\,dr = \frac{1}{2}\int_{\alpha}^{\beta} r^2\,d\theta, \text{ where } r = f(\theta).$$

Ex. 1. Find the area of a loop of the lemniscate whose equation is $r^2 = a^2\cos 2\theta$.

$$\text{Area} = \frac{1}{2}\int_{-\frac{\pi}{4}}^{\frac{\pi}{4}} r^2 d\theta = \frac{a^2}{2}\int_{-\frac{\pi}{4}}^{\frac{\pi}{4}} \cos 2\theta\,d\theta = \frac{a^2}{2}.$$

Ex. 2. The sphere $x^2+y^2+z^2 = a^2$ is pierced by the cylinder $x^2+y^2 = ay$. Find the volume enclosed by the two surfaces. This is known as Viviani's problem.

If V is the required volume

$$\frac{1}{2}V = \iint \sqrt{(a^2-x^2-y^2)}dx\,dy,$$

taken over the circle $x^2+y^2 = ay$. When this integral is changed into polar coordinates, it becomes

$$2\int_{0}^{\frac{\pi}{2}} d\theta \int_{0}^{a\sin\theta} \sqrt{(a^2-r^2)}rdr = 2\int_{0}^{\frac{\pi}{2}} \left[-\frac{1}{3}(a^2-r^2)^{\frac{3}{2}}\right]_{0}^{a\sin\theta} d\theta$$

$$= \frac{2}{3}\int_{0}^{\frac{\pi}{2}} (a^3-a^3\cos^3\theta)\,d\theta = \frac{2a^3}{3}\left(\frac{\pi}{2}-\frac{2}{3}\right).$$

Hence $V = \frac{2}{3}\left(\pi - \frac{4}{3}\right)a^3.$

In the case of the triplo integral

$$x = r \sin\theta \cos\phi,\ y = r \sin\theta \sin\phi,\ z = r\cos\theta,$$

where

$$r = OP,\ \theta = \angle ZOP,\ \phi = \angle XOM,$$

P being the point (x, y, z) and M the projection of P on the plane $z = 0$. Then

$$\frac{\partial(x, y, z)}{\partial(r, \theta, \phi)} = \begin{vmatrix} \sin\theta\cos\phi & \sin\theta\sin\phi & \cos\theta \\ r\cos\theta\cos\phi & r\cos\theta\sin\phi & -r\sin\theta \\ -r\sin\theta\sin\phi & r\sin\theta\cos\phi & 0 \end{vmatrix}$$

$$= r^2 \sin\theta,$$

and thus

$$\iiint f(x, y, z)\, dx\, dy\, dz = \iiint F(r, \theta, \phi) r^2 \sin\theta\, dr\, d\theta\, d\phi,$$

where

$$F(r, \theta, \phi) = f[r\sin\theta\cos\phi,\ r\sin\theta\sin\phi,\ r\cos\theta].$$

Note that $|\partial(x, y, z)/\partial(r, \theta, \phi)| = r^2\sin\theta$, since $\sin\theta$ is not negative for $0 \leqslant \theta \leqslant \pi$.

Ex. 1. Find the volume of the sphere of radius a.

$$\text{Volume} = \int_0^a r^2 dr \int_0^\pi \sin\theta\, d\theta \int_0^{2\pi} d\phi = \frac{4\pi}{3} a^3.$$

Ex. 2. Evaluate the triple integral of the function x^2y^2z throughout the portion of the cone $x^2+y^2 = xz$, which lies between the planes $z = 0$ and $z = c$.

$$\text{Integral} = 2\int_0^{\frac{\pi}{2}} d\phi \int_0^{\tan^{-1}(\cos\phi)} d\theta \int_0^{c/\cos\theta} \sin^5\theta\cos\theta\cos^2\phi\sin^2\phi\, r^7 dr$$

$$= \frac{c^8}{4}\int_0^{\frac{\pi}{2}} \cos^2\phi\sin^2\phi\, d\phi \int_0^{\tan^{-1}(\cos\phi)} \sin^5\theta\sec^7\theta\, d\theta$$

$$= \frac{c^8}{24}\int_0^{\frac{\pi}{2}} \cos^8\phi\sin^2\phi\, d\phi = \frac{7\pi}{48}\left(\frac{c}{2}\right)^8.$$

Examples II

1. Sketch the curve $y(x^2+y^2) = a(x^2-y^2)$, and find the area of the loop.

2. A sphere of radius a is pierced by a circular cylinder of cross-section with radius b, where $b<a$, the axis of the cylinder passing through the centre of the sphere. Find the volume of the sphere inside the cylinder.

3. Determine the volume of the part of the cylinder $x^2+y^2-2ax = 0$ cut off by the cylinder $z^2 = 2ax$.

4. Find the volume of the solid figure bounded by the paraboloid $x^2/a^2+y^2/b^2 = 2z$ and the plane $x+y+z = 1$.

5. Evaluate the integral

$$\int_0^a dx \int_0^{2a} \frac{dy}{(x^2+y^2+a^2)^2}.$$

6. Integrate the following functions throughout the volume of the ellipsoid $x^2/a^2+y^2/b^2+z^2/c^2 = 1$:

$$\text{(i) } e^{\sqrt{(x^2/a^2+y^2/b^2+z^2/c^2)}}, \quad \text{(ii) } (\lambda x+\mu y+\nu z)^{2n},$$

where n is a positive integer.

7. Show that

$$\int_0^\infty dx \int_0^\infty xy\, e^{-(x^2+y^2+2xy\cos\alpha)}\, dy = \frac{\sin\alpha-\alpha\cos\alpha}{4\sin^3\alpha},$$

where $0<\alpha<\pi$.

8. Prove that if $f(-x) = f(x)$

$$\iint f(ax+by)\sqrt{(c^2-x^2-y^2)}dx\,dy = \pi \int_0^c f(kx)(c^2-x^2)dx,$$

where the double integral is taken over the circle $x^2+y^2 = c^2$ and $k^2 = a^2+b^2$.

9. (i) Integrate the function $1/xy$ over the area bounded by the four circles $x^2+y^2 = ax,\ a'x,\ by,\ b'y$, where $a,\ a'$, $b,\ b'$ are positive.

(ii) Integrate the function $1/xyz$ throughout the volume bounded by the six spheres $x^2+y^2+z^2 = ax,\ a'x,\ by,\ b'y,\ cz,\ c'z$, where $a,\ a',\ b,\ b',\ c,\ c'$ are positive.

10. Integrate the function $y^2z^2+z^2x^2+x^2y^2$ through the volume of the cylinder $x^2+y^2-2ax = 0$ between the sheets of the cone $z^2 = k^2(x^2+y^2)$.

11. Find the mean value * of x^2 throughout the positive octant of the solid bounded by the surface $x^{\frac{2}{3}}+y^{\frac{2}{3}}+z^{\frac{2}{3}} = a^{\frac{2}{3}}$.

12. Find the volume of the solid bounded by the six cylinders.

$$z^2 = y,\ z^2 = 2y,\ x^2 = z,\ x^2 = 2z,\ y^2 = x,\ y^2 = 2x.$$

13. Show that

$$\iiint (x^3+y^3+z^3)dx\,dy\,dz = \frac{32}{5}\pi a^6,$$

the integral being taken throughout the interior of the sphere

$$x^2+y^2+z^2-2a(x+y+z)+2a^2 = 0.$$

14. Show that the volume of the solid figure bounded by the paraboloid $x^2-y^2 = 2az$, the cylinder $(x^2+y^2)^2 = a^2(x^2-y^2)$ and the plane $z = 0$ is $a^3/6$.

[Answers : 1. $\left(2-\frac{\pi}{2}\right)a^2$; 2. $\frac{4\pi}{3}\left\{a^3-(a^2-b^2)^{3/2}\right\}$; 3. $\frac{128}{15}a^3$;

4. $\frac{\pi ab(2+a^2+b^2)^2}{4}$; 5. $\frac{\sqrt{2}}{4a^2}\tan^{-1}\sqrt{2}+\frac{\sqrt{5}}{5a^2}\tan^{-1}\frac{\sqrt{5}}{5}$;

6. (i) $4\pi abc(e-2)$, (ii) $\frac{4\pi abc(\lambda^2a^2+\mu^2b^2+\nu^2c^2)^n}{(2n+1)(2n+3)}$;

9. (i) $\left|\log\frac{a'}{a}\log\frac{b'}{b}\right|$, (ii) $\left|\log\frac{a'}{a}\log\frac{b'}{b}\log\frac{c'}{c}\right|$;

10. $\frac{8192}{735}a^7k\left(k^2+\frac{8}{33}\right)$; 11. $\frac{7a^2}{143}$; 12. $\frac{1}{7}$].

* The mean value of the function $f(x, y, z)$ throughout the volume K is defined to be the value of $\iiint_K f(x, y, z)\,dx\,dy\,dz$ divided by the volume of K.

CHAPTER IV

CURVILINEAR AND SURFACE INTEGRALS

§ 18. Length of a Curve

IN Chapter I we showed how to use the limiting process to evaluate the area enclosed by a curve. We shall now show how to use this process to evaluate the length of a curve. If an n-sided regular polygon is inscribed in a circle, its perimeter can be calculated since it consists of a set of straight lines. As n increases we find that this length becomes more and more nearly equal to a definite number which is the length of the circumference of the circle.

We now proceed to find the length of the arc CD of the curve $y = f(x)$ in Fig. 2, p. 3. Let s denote the variable length of arc CP, where as before x is the abscissa of P. Then it is clear that s is a function of x, and we proceed to find ds/dx. Now Q is the point on the curve of abscissa $x+\Delta x$, the length of the arc CQ is $s+\Delta s$, and so the arc PQ has length Δs. But

$$(\text{chord } PQ)^2 = PS^2+SQ^2 = (\Delta x)^2+(\Delta y)^2;$$

hence

$$(\Delta s)^2 = \left(\frac{\text{arc } PQ}{\text{chord } PQ}\right)^2\left[(\Delta x)^2+(\Delta y)^2\right],$$

$$\text{i.e.}\quad \left(\frac{\Delta s}{\Delta x}\right)^2 = \left(\frac{\text{arc } PQ}{\text{chord } PQ}\right)^2\left[1+\left(\frac{\Delta y}{\Delta x}\right)^2\right].$$

Let $\Delta x \to 0$; then

$$\frac{\Delta y}{\Delta x} \to \frac{dy}{dx}, \quad \frac{\text{arc } PQ}{\text{chord } PQ} \to 1, \quad \frac{\Delta s}{\Delta x} \to \frac{ds}{dx},$$

and we have

$$\left(\frac{ds}{dx}\right)^2 = 1+\left(\frac{dy}{dx}\right)^2.$$

Thus the length of the arc CD is given by

$$\int_a^b \sqrt{\left\{1+\left(\frac{dy}{dx}\right)^2\right\}} dx.$$

If the equation of the curve is given by the freedom equations $x = x(t)$, $y = y(t)$, the length of the arc can be expressed as an integral with respect to the variable t.

Since $\dfrac{dy}{dx} = \dfrac{dy}{dt}\Big/\dfrac{dx}{dt}$, the length of the arc CD is

$$\int_{t_0}^{t_1} \sqrt{\left\{1+\left(\frac{dy/dt}{dx/dt}\right)^2\right\}} \frac{dx}{dt} dt,$$

$$\textit{i.e.} \quad \int_{t_0}^{t_1} \sqrt{\left\{\left(\frac{dx}{dt}\right)^2+\left(\frac{dy}{dt}\right)^2\right\}} dt,$$

where t_0, t_1 are the values of the parameter t at C and D.

If the equation of the curve is given in terms of polar coordinates r, θ, where $x = r\cos\theta$, $y = r\sin\theta$, we have

$$\frac{dx}{d\theta} = \frac{dr}{d\theta}\cos\theta - r\sin\theta, \quad \frac{dy}{d\theta} = \frac{dr}{d\theta}\sin\theta + r\cos\theta,$$

so that

$$\left(\frac{dx}{d\theta}\right)^2 + \left(\frac{dy}{d\theta}\right)^2 = \left(\frac{dr}{d\theta}\right)^2 + r^2.$$

Hence the length of an arc is given by

$$\int_{\theta_0}^{\theta_1} \sqrt{\left\{\left(\frac{dr}{d\theta}\right)^2 + r^2\right\}} d\theta,$$

where θ_0, θ_1 are the vectorial angles of the ends of the arc.

Ex. 1. To find the length of the circumference of a circle of radius a.

For the circle $x^2+y^2=a^2$, $2x+2y\dfrac{dy}{dx}=0$, and so $\dfrac{dy}{dx}=-\dfrac{x}{y}$. Hence the length of the circumference is

$$4\int_0^a\sqrt{\left(1+\frac{x^2}{y^2}\right)}dx=4a\int_0^a\frac{dx}{\sqrt{(a^2-x^2)}}=2\pi a.$$

Ex. 2. Show that the length of one arch of the cycloid whose freedom equations are $x=a(t-\sin t)$, $y=a(1-\cos t)$ is $8a$.

$$\text{Length of an arch}=2a\int_0^\pi\sqrt{\{(1-\cos t)^2+\sin^2 t\}}\,dt$$

$$=2a\int_0^\pi\sqrt{(2-2\cos t)}dt=4a\int_0^\pi\sin\frac{t}{2}\,dt=8a.$$

Ex. 3. Show that the length of the cardioid $r=2(1-\cos\theta)$ is 16 units.

$$\text{Length}=2\int_0^\pi\sqrt{\left\{\left(\frac{dr}{d\theta}\right)^2+r^2\right\}}\,d\theta$$

$$=2\int_0^\pi\sqrt{\{4\sin^2\theta+4(1-\cos\theta)^2\}}\,d\theta=\mathbf{16}.$$

§ 19. Curvilinear or Line Integrals

Let $F(x, y)$ be a function of the variables x and y, and let $y=f(x)$ be a single-valued function of x, represented in Fig. 2 by the curve CPD. Then the integral $\int_a^b F[x,f(x)]dx$ is written $\int_{CD} F(x,y)dx$ and is called the **curvilinear** or **line integral** $\int F(x,y)dx$ along the curve $y=f(x)$ from C to D.

Suppose further that the curve CPD is such that any line parallel to the x-axis meets it in only one point, *i.e.* its equation can be expressed in the form $x=\psi(y)$, where $\psi(y)$ is a single-valued function of y. If the ordinates of C and D are c and d, then $\int_c^d F[\psi(y), y]dy$ is the curvilinear integral $\int_{CD} F(x, y)dy$ along the curve from C to D.

A curvilinear integral may be taken in two directions along a curve; for example the arc CD may be taken from C to D or from D to C. We have

$$\int_{\mathbf{DC}} \mathbf{F(x, y)dx} = -\int_{\mathbf{CD}} \mathbf{F(x, y)dx},$$

for
$$\int_{DC} F(x, y)dx = \int_b^a F[x, f(x)]dx = -\int_a^b F[x, f(x)]dx$$
$$= -\int_{CD} F(x, y)dx.$$

In the case of a curve which is the boundary of an area in the plane we distinguish between the directions along the curve by means of the terms positive and negative. We define the positive direction to be such that **a person moving round the curve in the positive direction has the area enclosed by the curve on his left-hand side.**

As an example of a curvilinear integral let us take $\int y\,dx$ round the circle $x^2+y^2 = a^2$, the circuit being made in the positive direction. The integral may be divided into two parts:

(i) $\int_a^{-a} \sqrt{(a^2-x^2)}dx$, the integral over the semicircle lying above the x-axis,

(ii) $\int_{-a}^{a} -\sqrt{(a^2-x^2)}dx$, the integral over the semicircle lying below the x-axis.

The complete integral is therefore $-4\int_0^a \sqrt{(a^2-x^2)}dx$, *i.e.* $-\pi a^2$. If the integral is taken round the circle in the negative direction its value is πa^2.

The expression $\int\sqrt{\left\{1+\left(\frac{dy}{dx}\right)^2\right\}}dx$ which was given in the last paragraph for the length of a curve is a curvilinear integral. It may be put in the form $\int\frac{ds}{dx}dx$ or simply $\int ds$. A difficulty as to sign appears here. For the circle $x^2+y^2=a^2$ we saw that ds/dx is numerically equal to $a/\sqrt{(a^2-x^2)}$; if we take this value and integrate round the circle the result is clearly zero. To get over this difficulty we make the following convention as to sign. For a particular direction along a curve let θ be the angle which the forward direction of the tangent to the curve makes with the positive direction of the x-axis. Then we define ds to be $dx/\cos\theta$ in magnitude and sign. It is clear from a figure that with this definition ds is positive for both directions along the curve, and $\int ds$ gives the length of the curve no matter in which direction we integrate.

A curvilinear integral may appear in the form

$$\int_{AB} F(x, y)ds,$$

the integral of the function $F(x, y)$ along the curve from A to B. To evaluate this integral we express it as

$$\int_a^b F\left[x, f(x)\right]\frac{dx}{\cos\theta},$$

where $y=f(x)$ is the equation of the curve,

$$1/|\cos\theta| = \sqrt{\left\{1+\left(\frac{dy}{dx}\right)^2\right\}},$$

and the sign of $\cos\theta$ is taken into account. Let us now take the integral $\int_{BA} F(x, y)ds$; this is $\int_b^a F\left[x, f(x)\right]\frac{dx}{\cos\theta'},$

where $\cos\theta' = -\cos\theta$. Thus

$$\int_{\mathbf{BA}} \mathbf{F(x, y)ds} = \int_{\mathbf{AB}} \mathbf{F(x, y)ds},$$

i.e. $\int F(x, y)ds$ is independent of the direction in which we integrate along the curve.

Ex. Evaluate the integral $\int y\,ds$ round the circle $x^2+y^2=a^2$.

We may integrate in the positive direction starting from the point $(a, 0)$; the integral is

$$\int_a^{-a} +\sqrt{(a^2-x^2)} \cdot \frac{a\,dx}{-\sqrt{(a^2-x^2)}} + \int_{-a}^{a} -\sqrt{(a^2-x^2)} \cdot \frac{a\,dx}{+\sqrt{(a^2-x^2)}} = 0.$$

§ 20. Theorem

If P(x,y), Q(x,y) *are functions defined inside and on the boundary* C *of the closed area* K, *then*

$$\iint_{\mathrm{K}} \left(\frac{\partial \mathrm{Q}}{\partial \mathrm{x}} - \frac{\partial \mathrm{P}}{\partial \mathrm{y}}\right) \mathrm{dx\,dy} = \int_{\mathrm{C}} (\mathrm{P\,dx} + \mathrm{Q\,dy}),$$

where the curvilinear integral round C *is taken in the positive direction.*

We assume first of all that the curve C is such that any line parallel to the x and y axes meets it in at most two points and we take the curve $DEFG$ of Fig. 5, p. 34, to be the curve C. Then

$$\iint_K \frac{\partial Q}{\partial x}\,dx\,dy = \int_c^d dy \int_{QR}^{QR'} \frac{\partial Q}{\partial x}\,dx$$

$$= \int_c^d Q[\psi_2(y), y]dy - \int_c^d Q[\psi_1(y), y]dy$$

$$= \int_{DEF} Q(x, y)dy - \int_{DGF} Q(x, y)dy = \int_{DEF} Q\,dy + \int_{FGD} Q\,dy$$

$$= \int_C Q(x, y)dy, \text{ taken in the positive direction.}$$

Similarly,

$$\iint\limits_K \frac{\partial P}{\partial y} dx\,dy = \int_a^b dx \int_{MP}^{MP'} \frac{\partial P}{\partial y} dy$$

$$= \int_a^b P[x, \phi_2(x)]dx - \int_a^b P[x, \phi_1(x)]dx$$

$$= \int\limits_{GFE} P(x, y)dx - \int\limits_{GDE} P(x, y)dx = -\int\limits_{EFG} P\,dx - \int\limits_{GDE} P\,dx$$

$$= -\int\limits_C P(x, y)dx, \text{ taken in the positive direction.}$$

This proves the theorem in this case.

If the curve C is cut by some lines parallel to the axes in more than two points, we can divide the area into parts for which it is true that any line parallel to the axes cuts the boundary curve in not more than two parts. Apply the theorem to each of these parts and sum up the double and curvilinear integrals ; the double integrals are additive and the sum of the curvilinear integrals is the integral of $P\,dx+Q\,dy$ round C in the positive direction, since the integrals on the dividing lines cancel out.

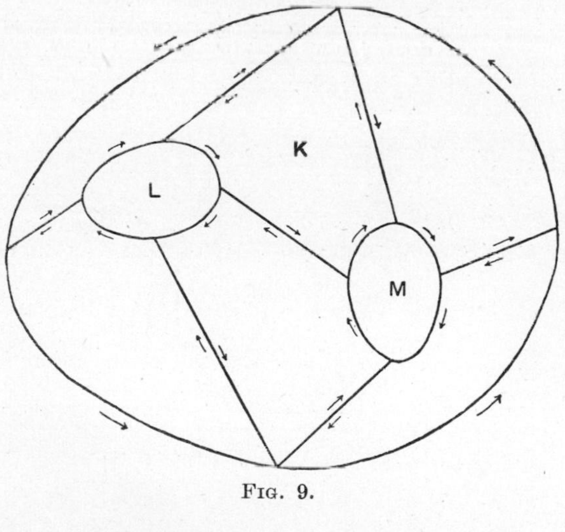

FIG. 9.

The theorem is still true even if the area K is not simply-connected, *i.e.* if there are closed areas inside the curve which are not parts of K. Fig. 9 shows the area K between an outer curve and two inner closed curves cutting off from K the areas L and M.

The method of division shown in the figure gives the result of the theorem, where the curvilinear integral is taken in the positive direction round the outer curve and in the negative direction round the areas L and M. This whole contour is still the positive direction round the area K.

Ex. 1. Show that the area of K is given by $\int_C x\,dy$, or $-\int_C y\,dx$, or $\frac{1}{2}\int_C (x\,dy-y\,dx)$, where in each case the curvilinear integral is taken in the positive direction round K.

Ex. 2. Prove that $\iint_K \left(\frac{\partial^2 V}{\partial x^2}+\frac{\partial^2 V}{\partial y^2}\right) dx\,dy = \int_C \frac{\partial V}{\partial n}\,ds$, where $\frac{\partial V}{\partial n}$ is the derivative of V in the direction of the outward normal to the curve C.*

In the theorem let $Q = \partial V/\partial x$, $P = -\partial V/\partial y$, and we have

$$\iint_K \left(\frac{\partial^2 V}{\partial x^2}+\frac{\partial^2 V}{\partial y^2}\right) dx\,dy = \int_C \left(\frac{\partial V}{\partial x}\,dy - \frac{\partial V}{\partial y}\,dx\right)$$

$= \int_C \left(\frac{\partial V}{\partial x}\frac{dy}{ds} - \frac{\partial V}{\partial y}\frac{dx}{ds}\right) ds$, where $\frac{dy}{ds}, \frac{dx}{ds}$ are respectively $\sin\theta$, $\cos\theta$, if θ is the angle which the positive direction of the tangent to the curve makes with the positive direction of the x-axis. But $\left(\frac{\partial V}{\partial x}\sin\theta - \frac{\partial V}{\partial y}\cos\theta\right)$ is the derivative of V in the direction of the outward normal to the curve. Hence the result.

* The derivative of a function $V(x,y)$ in a given direction is the rate of change of V with respect to distance measured in this direction.

§ 21. Surface of Revolution

In § 4 the volume of the solid figure bounded by a surface of revolution and two planes perpendicular to the axis of revolution was calculated. In this paragraph we show how to calculate the area of the curved surface of this solid figure. Let S denote the surface traced out by the arc CP in Fig. 2 (p. 3) as it revolves about the x-axis; then S is clearly a function of x, the abscissa of P. As x takes the increment Δx, S takes the increment ΔS, which is the area of the surface traced out by the arc PQ, denoted in § 18 by Δs. The chord PQ traces out the curved surface of a frustum of a cone with area $\pi(MP+NQ)PQ$. As $\Delta x \to 0$, $NQ \to MP$ and (arc PQ)/(chord PQ)$\to 1$. Therefore

$$\frac{dS}{dx} = 2\pi y \frac{ds}{dx},$$

and the area of the surface of revolution traced out by CD is

$$2\pi \int_a^b y\sqrt{\left\{1+\left(\frac{dy}{dx}\right)^2\right\}}dx.$$

Ex. To find the area of the surface of the paraboloid $y^2+z^2 = 4ax$ cut off by the plane $x = b$.

This paraboloid is obtained by revolving the parabola $y^2 = 4ax$ about the x-axis. Hence the surface area is

$$2\pi \int_0^b 2\sqrt{(ax)}\sqrt{\left(1+\frac{a}{x}\right)}dx = 4\pi\sqrt{a}\int_0^b \sqrt{(x+a)}dx$$

$$= \frac{8\pi\sqrt{a}}{3}\left[(a+b)^{\frac{3}{2}}-a^{\frac{3}{2}}\right].$$

§ 22. The Element of Surface

We shall now apply the method of double integration to find the area of the surface $z = f(x, y)$ cut off by a cylinder with generators parallel to the z-axis. Let the cylinder be that shown in Fig. 3 (p. 30) passing through the curve ABC in the plane $z = 0$ and cutting off from the surface the area bounded by the curve DEF. Let $Q(x, y)$ be a point lying in the area ABC and let a small rectangle in the plane $z = 0$ be taken with vertices (x, y), $(x+\Delta x, y)$, $(x+\Delta x, y+\Delta y)$, $(x, y+\Delta y)$; then the area of the rectangle is $\Delta x \Delta y$. Let P be the point on the surface of which Q is the projection, and let the tangent plane at P to the surface have its normal making an angle γ with the z-axis. Through the sides of the small rectangle in the plane $z=0$, let planes be drawn parallel to the z-axis cutting off a small area ΔS on the surface and a small parallelogram $\Delta S'$, on the tangent plane at P. Then the area of the parallelogram is given (apart from sign) by $\Delta x \ \Delta y / \ |\cos \gamma|$. Now as Δx and Δy tend to zero, $\Delta S/\Delta S'$ tends to 1, and we have the formula

$$\mathbf{dS} = \frac{\mathbf{dxdy}}{|\cos \gamma|},$$

where γ is the angle made with the z-axis by the normal to the surface at P, and dS is the element of surface at P. The area of the surface DEF is thus given by

$$\iint_{ABC} \frac{dx\,dy}{|\cos \gamma|}.$$

Now the direction cosines of the normal to the surface at P are proportional to $(p, q, -1)$, where $p = \dfrac{\partial z}{\partial x}$, $q = \dfrac{\partial z}{\partial y}$, and hence

$$|\cos \gamma| = \frac{1}{\sqrt{(1+p^2+q^2)}},$$

so that the surface area is

$$\iint_{\mathbf{ABC}} \sqrt{(\mathbf{1}+\mathbf{p}^2+\mathbf{q}^2)}\mathbf{dx\ dy}.$$

Ex. Find the area of the surface of the sphere $x^2+y^2+z^2=a^2$ which lies inside the cylinder $x^2+y^2 = ay$. (See Viviani's problem, p. 47.)

Here $p = -x/z$, $q = -y/z$;

$$\sqrt{(1+p^2+q^2)} = \sqrt{(1+x^2/z^2+y^2/z^2)} = a/\sqrt{(a^2-x^2-y^2)}.$$

Hence the required surface area is

$$4\iint \frac{a\,dx\,dy}{\sqrt{(a^2-x^2-y^2)}}, \text{ taken over half the circle } x^2+y^2 = ay$$

$$= 4a\int_0^{\frac{\pi}{2}} d\theta \int_0^{a\sin\theta} \frac{r\,dr}{\sqrt{(a^2-r^2)}} = 2(\pi-2)a^2.$$

§ 23. Freedom Equations of a Surface

The equations

$$x = x(u, v),\ y = y(u, v),\ z = z(u, v)\ .\ \ .\ \ .\quad (1)$$

are the freedom equations of a surface, because the result of eliminating the parameters u, v from these equations is an equation $F(x, y, z) = 0$, which represents a surface. Consider the set of values (u,v) which represent points lying in a given area A in the (u,v) plane. To this set of values there corresponds, by equations (1), a set of points lying on the surface and forming a surface area S. The problem is to obtain S as a double integral with respect to the variables u, v. We know from the last paragraph that the surface area is

$$\iint \sqrt{(1+p^2+q^2)}dx\,dy,$$

taken over the projection of the area on the plane $z = 0$, and we now use the transformation of § 16 to express this integral in terms of u and v. We express the integrand in terms of u, v and replace $dx\,dy$ by $[\partial(x, y)/\partial(u, v)]\,du\,dv$. Now

$$\frac{\partial z}{\partial u} = \frac{\partial z}{\partial x}\frac{\partial x}{\partial u} + \frac{\partial z}{\partial y}\frac{\partial y}{\partial u},\quad \frac{\partial z}{\partial v} = \frac{\partial z}{\partial x}\frac{\partial x}{\partial v} + \frac{\partial z}{\partial y}\frac{\partial y}{\partial v};$$

hence

$$\frac{\partial z}{\partial x} = -\frac{\partial(y, z)}{\partial(u, v)}\Big/\frac{\partial(x, y)}{\partial(u, v)},\quad \frac{\partial z}{\partial y} = -\frac{\partial(z, x)}{\partial(u, v)}\Big/\frac{\partial(x, y)}{\partial(u, v)}.$$

On substitution in the integral we obtain

$$\iint_{A} \sqrt{\left\{\left[\frac{\partial(\mathbf{y}, \mathbf{z})}{\partial(\mathbf{u}, \mathbf{v})}\right]^2 + \left[\frac{\partial(\mathbf{z}, \mathbf{x})}{\partial(\mathbf{u}, \mathbf{v})}\right]^2 + \left[\frac{\partial(\mathbf{x}, \mathbf{y})}{\partial(\mathbf{u}, \mathbf{v})}\right]^2\right\}}\, \mathbf{du}\, \mathbf{dv}$$

as the surface area represented by the set of values (u, v) lying in the given area A in the (u, v) plane.

If the surface is given by the spherical polar equation $r = f(\theta, \phi)$, we can use this result, taking θ, ϕ as parameters, to obtain the area of the surface. We have

$$\frac{\partial(y, z)}{\partial(\theta, \phi)} = r\frac{\partial r}{\partial \phi} \sin \phi - r\frac{\partial r}{\partial \theta} \sin\theta \cos\theta \cos\phi + r^2 \sin^2\theta \cos\phi,$$

$$\frac{\partial(z, x)}{\partial(\theta, \phi)} = -r\frac{\partial r}{\partial \phi} \cos \phi - r\frac{\partial r}{\partial \theta} \sin\theta \cos\theta \sin\phi + r^2 \sin^2\theta \sin\phi,$$

$$\frac{\partial(x, y)}{\partial(\theta, \phi)} = r\frac{\partial r}{\partial \theta} \sin^2\theta + r^2 \sin\theta \cos\theta,$$

and thus the area of the surface is given by

$$\iint \sqrt{\left[r^2 \left(\frac{\partial r}{\partial \phi}\right)^2 + r^2 \sin^2\theta \left(\frac{\partial r}{\partial \theta}\right)^2 + r^4 \sin^2\theta \right]}\, d\theta\, d\phi,$$

over the appropriate field of integration in the (θ, ϕ) plane.

§ 24. Surface Integrals

In § 19 we discussed integrals along a curve and we now extend the idea to integrals over a surface. These are called **surface integrals**. It will be remembered that we distinguished between $\int_{AB} F(x, y)dx$ and $\int_{BA} F(x, y)dx$ according to the direction along the curve in which we integrated. For a surface we make a similar distinction between the *sides* of the surface. We distinguish between the sides of a surface at a point on it by noting the directions of the normals to the surface drawn from the sides into the surrounding space. These normals are called the outward drawn normals to the sides of the surface.

We now proceed to define the surface integral

$$\iint F(x,y,z)dxdy$$

over a portion S of one side of the surface $z=f(x,y)$. We assume that the function $f(x,y)$ is single-valued, so that any line parallel to the z-axis meets the surface in only one point. Let A be the area in the plane $z=0$ which is the projection on this plane of the portion S of the surface. Let γ be the angle which the outward drawn normal to a particular side of the surface at a point on the surface makes with the z-axis. For one side of the surface, the "upper" side, $\cos\gamma$ is clearly positive, and for the other, the "lower" side, $\cos\gamma$ is negative. Thus the sign of $\cos\gamma$ distinguishes between the sides of the surface. The surface integral

$$\iint F(x, y, z)dx\,dy$$

over the portion S of the side of the surface $z=f(x,y)$ for which $\cos\gamma$ is positive is defined to be

$$+\iint_A F[x, y, f(x,y)]dx\,dy,$$

and for the side for which $\cos\gamma$ is negative it is defined to be

$$-\iint_A F[x, y, f(x,y)]dx\,dy$$

Thus the surface integral over one side is equal in magnitude but opposite in sign to the surface integral over the other side.

As an example we take $\displaystyle\iint \frac{dx\,dy}{z}$ over the outside of the sphere $x^2+y^2+z^2=a^2$. For the portion above the plane $z=0$ the surface integral is

$$+\iint \frac{dx\,dy}{+\sqrt{(a^2-x^2-y^2)}}$$

over the circle $x^2+y^2=a^2$; for the portion below the plane $z=0$ the surface integral is

$$-\iint\frac{dx\,dy}{-\sqrt{(a^2-x^2-y^2)}}.$$

Hence the surface integral over the whole of the outside of the sphere is $2\iint\frac{dx\,dy}{\sqrt{(a^2-x^2-y^2)}}$ over the circle, *i.e.* $4\pi a$.

We define similarly

$$\iint F(x,y,z)dy\,dz \text{ and} \iint F(x,y,z)dz\,dx.$$

In § 19 we saw that $\int F(x,y)ds$ is independent of the direction in which we integrate along the curve. We now define the analogous surface integral

$$\iint F(x,y,z)dS$$

over the portion S of the surface $z=f(x,y)$ as

$$\iint\limits_A F[x,y,f(x,y)]\,\frac{dx\,dy}{|\cos\gamma|},$$

where γ is the angle which either of the outward drawn normals makes with the z-axis. It is clear from this definition that this surface integral does not depend on a particular side of the surface.

Ex. Show that the integral

$$\iint\frac{1}{xyz}\,(yz\,dydz+zx\,dzdx+xy\,dxdy),$$

taken over the outside of the surface of the ellipsoid $x^2/a^2+y^2/b^2+z^2/c^2=1$, has the value $\frac{4\pi}{abc}(b^2c^2+c^2a^2+a^2b^2)$.

§ 25. Gauss's Theorem *

In § 20 we proved a theorem giving a connection between a double integral over an area and a curvilinear integral round the boundary of the area. We now prove

* For alternative treatment see Rutherford, *Vector Methods*, p. 64. In older books this theorem is often called Green's theorem.

an extension of this theorem giving a relation between a triple integral throughout a volume and a surface integral over the boundary surface of the volume.

If P(x, y, z), Q(x, y, z), R(x, y, z) *are functions defined in and on the boundary of the solid figure* K *bounded by the surface* S, *then*

$$\iiint_K \left(\frac{\partial P}{\partial x} + \frac{\partial Q}{\partial y} + \frac{\partial R}{\partial z}\right) dx\, dy\, dz = \iint_S (P\, dy\, dz + Q\, dz\, dx + R\, dx\, dy),$$

where the surface integral is taken over the outside of the surface S.

The proof is similar to that of § 20. We assume that any line parallel to the coordinate axes meets S in at most two points. As before, if this is not so, we divide the figure into portions for which it is true. The surface S is thus in two portions, the upper one having equation $z = \psi_2(x, y)$ and the lower $z = \psi_1(x, y)$ (using the notation of § 15, p. 39). Then

$$\iiint_K \frac{\partial R}{\partial z}\, dx\, dy\, dz = \int_a^b dx \int_{\phi_1(x)}^{\phi_2(x)} dy \int_{\psi_1(x, y)}^{\psi_2(x, y)} \frac{\partial R}{\partial z} dz$$

$$= \int_a^b dx \int_{\phi_1(x)}^{\phi_2(x)} R[x, y, \psi_2(x, y)] dy - \int_a^b dx \int_{\phi_1(x)}^{\phi_2(x)} R[x, y, \psi_1(x, y)] dy.$$

The first of these integrals is the surface integral $\iint R\, dx\, dy$ over the upper side of the surface $z = \psi_2(x, y)$ and the second, $-\iint R\, dx\, dy$, is the surface integral over the lower side of the surface $z = \psi_1(x, y)$. Thus

$$\iiint \frac{\partial R}{\partial z}\, dx\, dy\, dz = \iint_S R\, dx\, dy,$$

over the outside of the surface S. We treat the other parts of the triple integral similarly, and obtain

$$\iiint\limits_K \left(\frac{\partial P}{\partial x}+\frac{\partial Q}{\partial y}+\frac{\partial R}{\partial z}\right)dx\,dy\,dz = \iint\limits_S (P\,dy\,dz+Q\,dz\,dx+R\,dx\,dy),$$

over the outside of S. As in the previous case, the surface integrals over the dividing surfaces cancel out and the theorem holds for any closed figure.

Ex. 1. Show that the volume of K is given by each of the surface integrals $\iint\limits_S x\,dy\,dz$, $\iint\limits_S y\,dz\,dx$, $\iint\limits_S z\,dx\,dy$, where the integration takes place over the outside of S.

Ex. 2. Prove that

(i) $$\iiint\limits_K \Delta^2 u\,dx\,dy\,dz = \iint\limits_S \frac{\partial u}{\partial n}\,dS,$$

(ii) $$\iiint\limits_K (u\Delta^2 v - v\Delta^2 u)dx\,dy\,dz = \iint\limits_S \left(u\frac{\partial v}{\partial n} - v\frac{\partial u}{\partial n}\right)dS,$$

where $\Delta^2 u \equiv \frac{\partial^2 u}{\partial x^2}+\frac{\partial^2 u}{\partial y^2}+\frac{\partial^2 u}{\partial z^2}$ and $\frac{\partial u}{\partial n}$ is the derivative of u in the direction of the outward normal to the outside of the surface S.

Examples III

1. Show that the length of that part of the curve

$$x = a\sin^3 t,\ y = a\cos^3 t,$$

which lies in the first quadrant, is $3a/2$.

2. Find the total length of the curve

$$8y^2 = x^2(1-x^2),$$

and the area of the surface of revolution formed by revolving the curve about the x-axis.

3. Show that, when $AB>H^2$,

$$\int\limits_C \frac{x\,dy-y\,dx}{Ax^2+2Hxy+By^2} = 2\omega,$$

where C is the circle $x^2+y^2 = a^2$, ω is the area of the ellipse

$Ax^2+2Hxy+By^2 = 1$, and the line integral is described in the anti-clockwise direction.

4. Sketch the curve $y = -\log(1-x^2)$, and show that the length of the arc measured from the origin to the point on the curve whose abscissa is x is

$$\log\left(\frac{1+x}{1-x}\right)-x.$$

5. Prove that the surface of the solid formed by the revolution about the initial line of the curve

$$r^2 = a^2\cos^2\theta+b^2\sin^2\theta$$

is, if $a^2>b^2$ and $c^4 = a^4-b^4$,

$$2\pi\left(a^2+\frac{b^4}{c^2}\log\frac{a^2+c^2}{b^2}\right).$$

6. Find the area of that part of the cone $z^2 = x^2+y^2$ which lies inside the cylinder $x^2+y^2 = 2x$.

7. Find the area of the part of the surface $z^2 = 2xy$ which lies inside the sphere $x^2+y^2+z^2 = a^2$.

8. Find the area of the part of the paraboloid $x^2+y^2 = 2z$ which lies inside the cylinder $(x^2+y^2)^2 = x^2-y^2$.

9. Show that the surface area of the portion of the cone $x^2+y^2-xz = 0$ which lies between the planes $z = 0$ and $z = c$ is given by

$$c^2\int_0^{\frac{\pi}{2}}\sqrt{(1+\cos^4\theta)}d\theta.$$

10. Show that the integral $\iint(y^2z^2+z^2x^2+x^2y^2)dS$ taken over the surface intercepted on the upper half of the cone $z^2 = k^2(x^2+y^2)$ by the cylinder $x^2+y^2-2ax = 0$ has the value $\pi a^6(80k^2+7)\sqrt{(k^2+1)}/24$.

11. Prove that the mean value of $(ax+by+cz)^{2n}$ over the surface of the sphere $x^2+y^2+z^2 = 1$ is $(a^2+b^2+c^2)^n/(2n+1)$.

12. If p is the length of the perpendicular from the origin on the tangent plane at any point on the surface $4x^2+4y^2+z^2 = 4a^2$, prove that the value of the integral $\iint(1/p)\,dS$ taken over the surface is $6\pi a$.

13. Show that the area of the surface of the cylindroid

$$x = r\cos\theta,\ y = r\sin\theta,\ z = a\sin\theta\cos\theta$$

contained within the cylinder $x^2+y^2 = b^2$ can be expressed in the form

$$S = 4\int_0^b \sqrt{(r^2+a^2)}E\left(k, \frac{\pi}{2}\right) dr,$$

where $E\left(k, \frac{\pi}{2}\right) = \int_0^{\frac{\pi}{2}} \sqrt{(1-k^2\sin^2\phi)}d\phi,\ k = \frac{a}{\sqrt{(r^2+a^2)}}.$

14. Prove that the surface of the oblate spheroid obtained by rotating an ellipse of semi-axes a and b $(b<a)$ about its minor axis is

$$2\pi a^2 + \frac{\pi b^2}{e}\log\frac{1+e}{1-e},$$

where e is the eccentricity of the ellipse.

15. Show that the area of the part of the surface of the paraboloid $x^2-y^2 = 2az$ which lies within the cylinder $(x^2+y^2)^2 = a^2(x^2-y^2)$ is $\frac{a^2}{9}(20-3\pi)$.

$\left[\text{Answers: } 2.\ \sqrt{2}\pi,\ \frac{\pi}{2},\ 6.\ 2\sqrt{2}\pi,\ 7.\ \sqrt{2}\pi a^2,\ 8.\ \frac{20}{9} - \frac{\pi}{3}.\right]$

CHAPTER V

THE RIEMANN INTEGRAL

§ 26. In this chapter we return to the definition of the integral and attempt to put the whole discussion on a more rigorous basis. In Chapter I the integral of the function $f(x)$ between the limits a and b was defined as the measure of the area between the x-axis, the lines $x = a$, $x = b$ and the curve $y = f(x)$. This definition is unsatisfactory for several reasons. The most important is that it is implied that the " area " of a field bounded by curves has some *a priori* meaning and can be measured. The proper method is to define the integral in some arithmetical way and define the area as the integral. It was Riemann (1826-1866) who gave the rigorous analytical definition of the integral which will be expounded in this chapter. We shall require certain elementary ideas and results from the theory of functions of a real variable.

§ 27. Preliminary Definitions

Throughout this and the subsequent chapters it is to be understood that ϵ and η are non zero positive numbers.

(1) We say that the **limit** of $f(x)$ as x tends to a is L if, given any ϵ, we can find η such that

$$|f(x)-L| < \epsilon \text{ for all values of } x \text{ satisfying } |x-a| < \eta.$$

This is written

$$\lim_{x \to a} f(x) = L.$$

It should be noted that the *value* of $f(x)$ when $x = a$ is not to be taken into account; in fact $f(x)$ need not be defined for $x = a$.

(2) We say that the limit of $f(x)$ as x tends to infinity is L, if, given any ϵ, we can find a positive number N such that

$$|f(x)-L| < \epsilon \text{ for all values of } x \text{ greater than } N.$$

This is written

$$\lim_{x \to \infty} f(x) = L.$$

(3) The **derivative** of $f(x)$ at the point x_0 is defined to be

$$\lim_{h \to 0} \frac{f(x_0+h)-f(x_0)}{h},$$

when this limit exists.

(4) A set of numbers is **bounded above** if there exists a number K greater than every number of the set, and it is **bounded below** if there exists a number K' less than every number of the set. The set is **bounded** if it is bounded above and below. The **upper bound** of a set of numbers is the smallest number which is not exceeded by any member of the set, and the **lower bound** of a set is the greatest number below which no member of the set lies. We shall assume the fundamental theorem on bounded sets which states that a set which is bounded above possesses an upper bound and that a set which is bounded below possesses a lower bound. The most usual sets of numbers with which we shall deal are the sets of values of functions defined in given intervals. For example, we say that $f(x)$ is bounded above in the interval $a \leqslant x \leqslant b$ if there exists a number K greater than every value of $f(x)$ in the interval.

(5) The function $f(x)$, defined in the interval $a \leqslant x \leqslant b$, is said to be **continuous at the point** x_0 of the interval if

$$\lim_{x \to x_0} f(x) = f(x_0),$$

i.e. given any ϵ, we can find η such that

$$|f(x)-f(x_0)| < \epsilon, \text{ whenever } |x-x_0| < \eta \text{ and } a \leqslant x \leqslant b.$$

A function is **continuous in an interval** if it is continuous at every point of the interval.

The function $f(x)$ is **uniformly continuous in the interval** $a \leqslant x \leqslant b$ if

(*a*) it is defined at every point of the interval,

(*b*) given any ϵ, we can find η such that

$$|f(x)-f(x_0)|<\epsilon, \text{ whenever } |x-x_0|<\eta, \ a \leqslant x \leqslant b,$$

where η is independent of x_0.

The theorem of uniform continuity states that when a function is continuous in an interval which includes its end-points (*e.g.* $a \leqslant x \leqslant b$) it is uniformly continuous in this interval. Further, it can be shown that in such an interval, called a **closed** interval, a continuous function is bounded and the bounds are values of the function. Any number lying between the bounds is a value of the function in the interval.

(6) The function $f(x, y)$, defined in a region A of the (x, y) plane, is said to be **continuous with respect to the pair of variables** (x, y) **at the point** (x_0, y_0) **of the region** if, given any ϵ, we can find η such that

$$|f(x, y)-f(x_0, y_0)|<\epsilon, \text{ whenever } |x-x_0|<\eta, \ |y-y_0|<\eta$$

and (x, y) belongs to A.

§ 28. Definition of the Integral

Let $f(x)$ be a function defined and bounded in the interval $a \leqslant x \leqslant b$. We divide the interval into a finite number of parts, not necessarily equal, by points $x_0, x_1, \ldots, x_n$, where $a = x_0 < x_1 < x_2 < \ldots < x_n = b$, and form the sum

$$\Sigma = \sum_{r=1}^{n} f(\xi_r)\delta_r,$$

where $\delta_r = x_r - x_{r-1}$ and ξ_r is any point of the sub-interval (x_{r-1}, x_r).

If a number I exists with the property that, given any ϵ, we can find η such that $|I - \Sigma| < \epsilon$, provided only that $\delta_r < \eta$ for all r concerned, then the function $f(x)$ is said to be **integrable** over the interval (a,b), and I is the integral of $f(x)$ with respect to x over (a,b).

It should be noted that I is not an ordinary limit because Σ is not an ordinary function. It varies if we alter the number or position of the points of division of (a,b) and also if we alter the positions of the points ξ_r in the sub-intervals. For the integral to exist it is necessary that $|I - \Sigma| < \epsilon$ for every way of dividing (a,b) in which $\delta_r < \eta$ and for every way of choosing ξ_r. In order to discuss this limit we introduce the **upper** and **lower sums** of $f(x)$ corresponding to any method of dividing (a,b) into sub-intervals. Let us take any particular method of dividing (a,b) into sub-intervals (x_{r-1}, x_r), and let M_r, m_r be the upper and lower bounds of $f(x)$ in (x_{r-1}, x_r). The upper and lower sums $\mathbf{S}$, $\mathbf{s}$ for this way of dividing (a,b) are defined by

$$\mathbf{S} = \sum_{r=1}^{n} M_r \delta_r, \quad \mathbf{s} = \sum_{r=1}^{n} m_r \delta_r.$$

The values of $\mathbf{S}$, $\mathbf{s}$ are thus dependent only on the method of dividing (a, b). In the example illustrated by Fig. 1 (p. 2), $f(x) = \sqrt{(a^2 - x^2)}$ and the sums $\mathbf{S}$, $\mathbf{s}$ there mentioned are the upper and lower sums of this function in the interval $(0, a)$ for the method of division chosen.

We now use the upper and lower sums to prove the fundamental theorem on the existence of the integral.

§ 29. Theorem

If, given any ϵ, *we can find* η *such that, for all methods of dividing* (a, b) *in which* $\delta_r < \eta$, $|\mathbf{S} - \mathbf{s}| < \epsilon$, *then* f(x) *is integrable over* (a, b).

No matter how the point ξ_r is chosen in the interval (x_{r-1}, x_r), $m_r \leqslant f(\xi_r) \leqslant M_r$, so that

$$\Sigma m_r \delta_r \leqslant \Sigma f(\xi_r) \delta_r \leqslant \Sigma M_r \delta_r,$$

i.e.
$$\mathbf{s} \leqslant \Sigma \leqslant \mathbf{S}. \quad . \quad . \quad . \quad . \quad . \quad (1)$$

Again, if m, M are the lower and upper bounds of $f(x)$ in (a, b), $m \leqslant m_r \leqslant M_r \leqslant M$ for every r, and hence

$$\Sigma m \delta_r \leqslant \Sigma m_r \delta_r \leqslant \Sigma M_r \delta_r \leqslant \Sigma M \delta_r,$$

i.e.
$$m(b-a) \leqslant \mathbf{s} \leqslant \mathbf{S} \leqslant M(b-a). \quad . \quad . \quad . \quad . \quad (2)$$

Let us now add new points of division to those already present and form corresponding lower and upper sums $\mathbf{s}_1$, $\mathbf{S}_1$. If, as a result, δ_r is now divided into parts $\delta_r^1, \delta_r^2, \ldots, \delta_r^k$ and if m_r^p, M_r^p are the bounds of $f(x)$ in δ_r^p, then, by (2),

$$m_r \delta_r \leqslant \sum_{p=1}^{k} m_r^p \delta_r^p \leqslant \sum_{p=1}^{k} M_r^p \delta_r^p \leqslant M_r \delta_r,$$

and on summing over (a, b)

$$\mathbf{s} \leqslant \mathbf{s}_1 \leqslant \mathbf{S}_1 \leqslant \mathbf{S}. \quad . \quad . \quad . \quad . \quad . \quad (3)$$

We shall now show that every lower sum is less than or equal to every upper sum, no matter how the interval is divided. This will be proved if we take any two ways of dividing (a, b), form corresponding sums $\mathbf{s}_1$, $\mathbf{S}_1$ and $\mathbf{s}_2$, $\mathbf{S}_2$, and show that $\mathbf{s}_1 \leqslant \mathbf{S}_2$. We take all the points of division for both methods and form sums $\mathbf{s}_3$, $\mathbf{S}_3$ for this new mode of division. Then, by (3),

$$\mathbf{s}_1 \leqslant \mathbf{s}_3 \leqslant \mathbf{S}_3 \leqslant \mathbf{S}_2.$$

From the result (2) it follows that the set of upper sums has a lower bound J and that the set of lower sums has an upper bound I [see § 27, (4)], and, since every lower sum is less than or equal to every upper sum, $I \leqslant J$. Now we are given that $|\mathbf{S}-\mathbf{s}| < \epsilon$ for all modes of division in which $\delta_r < \eta$; hence, since $\mathbf{s} \leqslant I \leqslant J \leqslant \mathbf{S}$, we have $J-I < \epsilon$.

But J and I are definite numbers and ϵ is arbitrary ; thus J and I are equal. Again, for any particular method of division $\mathbf{s} \leqslant \Sigma \leqslant \mathbf{S}$, so that $|\Sigma - J| < \epsilon$, if only $\delta_r < \eta$. Thus the integral of $f(x)$ over (a, b) exists and is equal to J.

§ 30. Integration of Continuous Functions

We prove the following theorem.

If f(x) *is continuous in the interval* $a \leqslant x \leqslant b$, *it is integrable over this interval.*

By the theorem of uniform continuity, given any ϵ, we can find η, the same for all x_0 in (a, b) such that

$$|f(x) - f(x_0)| < \epsilon/(b-a), \text{ if } |x - x_0| < \eta.$$

We now divide (a, b) in any way into intervals δ_r such that $\delta_r < \eta$ for every r. The upper and lower bounds M_r, m_r of $f(x)$ in δ_r are values of $f(x)$, $f(\xi_r)$ and $f(\xi_r')$ say, where ξ_r and ξ_r' belong to δ_r. Hence

$$\mathbf{S} - \mathbf{s} = \sum_{r=1}^{n} (M_r - m_r)\delta_r = \sum_{r=1}^{n} [f(\xi_r) - f(\xi_r')]\delta_r.$$

Again, $|\xi_r - \xi_r'| < \eta$, since ξ_r, ξ_r' are in δ_r and $\delta_r < \eta$, so that $f(\xi_r) - f(\xi_r') < \epsilon/(b-a)$. Thus

$$\mathbf{S} - \mathbf{s} < \frac{\epsilon}{b-a} \Sigma \delta_r = \epsilon,$$

which proves that $f(x)$ is integrable over (a, b).

Let us suppose that $f(x)$ is continuous in the interval $a \leqslant x \leqslant b$ except for a finite discontinuity at $x = c$, where $a < c < b$; *i.e.*

$$\lim_{\epsilon \to 0} f(c - \epsilon) = H, \qquad \lim_{\epsilon \to 0} f(c + \epsilon) = K,$$

where H and K are finite and $H \neq K$. We now show that $f(x)$ is integrable over the interval (a, b). In any division of (a, b) into sub-intervals the point $x = c$ appears in at most two of the sub-intervals. The contribution to $\mathbf{S} - \mathbf{s}$ from these intervals is less than $2(M - m)$. max. δ_r, where

M, m are the upper and lower bounds of $f(x)$ in (a, b), and this can be made as small as we please. As above, $\mathbf{S}-\mathbf{s}<\epsilon$ for the remaining intervals, and so the integral exists. Similarly, if $f(x)$ has a finite number of discontinuities in (a, b), it is integrable over (a, b).

It may happen that $f(x)$ is continuous in the interval $a<x\leqslant b$, and that $f(a)$ does not exist. Similar reasoning to the above shows that if $\lim\limits_{\epsilon\to 0} f(a+\epsilon)$ is a finite number, $f(x)$ is integrable over (a, b).

§ 31. Properties of the Integral

Since the integral defined in § 28 is not an ordinary limit, we cannot apply the usual limit theorems of the differential calculus, and so it is difficult to deduce properties of the integral directly from the definition. However, if we assume that the integral exists, the following procedure enables us to express it as an ordinary limit, and we can deduce important properties of the integral.

Let a rule be given which specifies for each integral value of n one particular way of dividing (a, b) into n parts δ_r^n and one way of choosing ξ_r^n in δ_r^n. Thus

$$\Sigma_n = \sum_{r=1}^{n} f(\xi_r^n)\delta_r^n$$

depends only on n, and given any ϵ, we can find η such that $|I-\Sigma_n|<\epsilon$ if only each $\delta_r^n<\eta$, so that

$$I = \lim_{n\to\infty} \Sigma_n.$$

In particular we may divide (a, b) into n equal parts and take ξ_r^n as the right-hand end-point of each subinterval. Hence

$$\int_a^b f(x)dx = \lim_{n\to\infty} \delta[f(a+\delta)+f(a+2\delta)+ \dots +f(a+n\delta)],$$

where $\delta = (b-a)/n$. In passing we may note that if we

know by other means the value of the integral, this procedure gives us a method of evaluating certain limits.

For example, if we know that $\int_0^1 \frac{dx}{1+x} = \log 2$, we have

$$\lim_{n\to\infty}\left[\frac{1}{n+1}+\frac{1}{n+2}+\ldots+\frac{1}{2n}\right] = \lim_{n\to\infty}\frac{1}{n}\sum_{r=1}^{n}\frac{1}{1+r/n}$$
$$= \int_0^1 \frac{dx}{1+x} = \log 2.$$

We now prove the following properties of the integral.

(1) *If* k *is a constant and* $\int_a^b f(x)dx$ *exists, then* $\int_a^b kf(x)dx$ *exists and is equal to* $k\int_a^b f(x)dx$.

If, for any subdivision of (a, b) in which $\delta_r<\eta$, we have $\mathbf{S}-\mathbf{s}$ for $f(x)$ less than ϵ, then, for the same subdivision of (a, b), we clearly have $\mathbf{S}-\mathbf{s}$ for $kf(x)$ less than $|k|\epsilon$. Thus $kf(x)$ is integrable. We now apply the above procedure.

$$\int_a^b kf(x)dx = \lim_{n\to\infty}\sum_{r=1}^{n} kf(\xi_r^n)\delta_r^n = k\lim_{n\to\infty}\sum_{r=1}^{n} f(\xi_r^n)\delta_r^n$$
$$= k\int_a^b f(x)dx.$$

(2) *If* $a\leqslant\alpha\leqslant\beta\leqslant b$ *and* $\int_a^b f(x)dx$ *exists, then* $\int_\alpha^\beta f(x)dx$ *exists.*

If $\mathbf{S}-\mathbf{s}<\epsilon$ for any division of (a, b) in which $\delta_r<\eta$, it is clear that $\mathbf{S}-\mathbf{s}<\epsilon$ for any division of (α, β) in which $\delta_r<\eta$. Hence the integral exists.

(3) *If* f(x) *and* g(x) *are integrable over* (a,b), *then* $\int_a^b [f(x)+g(x)]dx$ *exists and is equal to* $\int_a^b f(x)dx+\int_a^b g(x)dx$.

If $\mathbf{s}_1$, $\mathbf{S}_1$, and $\mathbf{s}_2$, $\mathbf{S}_2$ denote the sums of $f(x)$ and $g(x)$ respectively, it is clear that

$$\mathbf{s}_1+\mathbf{s}_2\leqslant\mathbf{s}\leqslant\mathbf{S}\leqslant\mathbf{S}_1+\mathbf{S}_2,$$

where $\mathbf{s}$, $\mathbf{S}$ are the sums of $f(x)+g(x)$. Hence, if

$$\mathbf{S}_1-\mathbf{s}_1<\epsilon,\ \mathbf{S}_2-\mathbf{s}_2<\epsilon,$$

it follows that

$$\mathbf{S}-\mathbf{s}\leqslant\mathbf{S}_1+\mathbf{S}_2-\mathbf{s}_1-\mathbf{s}_2<2\epsilon,$$

so that $f(x)+g(x)$ is integrable. Again,

$$\begin{aligned}\int_a^b[f(x)+g(x)]dx &= \lim_{n\to\infty}\sum_{r=1}^{n}[f(\xi_r^n)+g(\xi_r^n)]\delta_r^n\\ &= \lim_{n\to\infty}\sum_{r=1}^{n}f(\xi_r^n)\delta_r^n+\lim_{n\to\infty}\sum_{r=1}^{n}g(\xi_r^n)\delta_r^n\\ &= \int_a^b f(x)dx+\int_a^b g(x)dx.\end{aligned}$$

(4) *If* f(x) *is integrable over* (a, b) *and* a<c<b,

$$\int_a^c f(x)dx+\int_c^b f(x)dx=\int_a^b f(x)dx.$$

By (2) $\int_a^c f(x)dx$ and $\int_c^b f(x)dx$ exist. If we form sums like Σ_n for the intervals (a, c) and (c, b), then $\Sigma_n(a, c)+\Sigma_n(c, b)$ is a sum like Σ_{2n} for (a, b) and when $n\to\infty$ the result follows.

(5) *If* f(x)$\geqslant$g(x) *and* f(x), g(x) *are integrable over* (a, b),

$$\int_a^b f(x)dx\geqslant\int_a^b g(x)dx.$$

This may be proved by taking sums like Σ_n for $f(x)$ and $g(x)$ using the same δ_r^n and ξ_r^n in each sum; then since $f(\xi_r^n)\geqslant g(\xi_r^n)$,

$$\sum_{r=1}^{n}f(\xi_r^n)\delta_r^n\geqslant\sum_{r=1}^{n}g(\xi_r^n)\delta_r^n,$$

and the result follows on letting $n\to\infty$.

(6) *If* f(x) *is integrable over* (a, b), |f(x)| *is integrable over* (a, b) *and*

$$\int_a^b |f(x)|dx \geqslant \left| \int_a^b f(x)dx \right|.$$

If M_r, m_r and M'_r, m'_r are the bounds of $f(x)$ and $|f(x)|$ respectively in δ_r, we have $M_r - m_r \geqslant M'_r - m'_r$; hence $\mathbf{S}-\mathbf{s}$ for $|f(x)|$ is less than or equal to $\mathbf{S}-\mathbf{s}$ for $f(x)$, i.e. $|f(x)|$ is integrable over (a, b). The second part of the result follows at once from (5).

(7) *If* f(x) *is integrable over* (a, b), *the function*

$$F(x) = \int_a^x f(t)dt$$

is continuous in (a, b).

By (2) the function $F(x)$ exists in (a, b).

To prove continuity we first note that

$$m(b-a) \leqslant \int_a^b f(x)dx \leqslant M(b-a),$$

where m, M are the bounds of $f(x)$ in (a, b). This follows at once from the definition of the sum Σ in § 28.

Given any ϵ, if $|x-x_0| < \epsilon/M'$, where M' is the upper bound of $|f(x)|$ in (a, b), then

$$|F(x)-F(x_0)| = \left| \int_{x_0}^x f(x)dx \right| \leqslant \left| \int_{x_0}^x |f(x)|dx \right| < \epsilon.$$

This proves the result.

(8) *If* f(x) *is continuous in the interval* $a \leqslant x \leqslant b$, *there is a number* ξ *in the interval such that*

$$\int_a^b f(x)dx = (b-a)f(\xi).$$

As in (7)

$$m \leqslant \frac{1}{b-a} \int_a^b f(x)dx \leqslant M.$$

It follows from the result mentioned in § 27, (5) that since $f(x)$ is continuous there is a number ξ, $a \leqslant \xi \leqslant b$, such that

$$f(\xi) = \frac{1}{b-a}\int_a^b f(x)dx.$$

(9) *If* f(x) *is continuous in the interval* $\mathrm{a} \leqslant \mathrm{x} \leqslant \mathrm{b}$, $\dfrac{\mathrm{d}}{\mathrm{dx}}\displaystyle\int_{\mathrm{a}}^{\mathrm{x}} \mathrm{f(t)dt}$ *exists and is* f(x).

We have

$$\frac{d}{dx}\int_a^x f(t)dt = \lim_{h\to 0}\frac{1}{h}\left[\int_a^{x+h} f(t)dt - \int_a^x f(t)dt\right],$$

if this limit exists. The limit is

$$\begin{aligned}\lim_{h\to 0}\frac{1}{h}\int_x^{x+h} f(t)dt &= \lim_{h\to 0} f(x+\theta h),\ (0\leqslant\theta\leqslant 1)\\ &= f(x).\end{aligned}$$

This result is known as the *Fundamental Theorem of the Integral Calculus.*

(10) *If* $\dfrac{\mathrm{d}}{\mathrm{dx}}\mathrm{F(x)} = \mathrm{f(x)}$ *and if* f(x) *is continuous in the interval* $\mathrm{a} \leqslant \mathrm{x} \leqslant \mathrm{b}$,

$$\int_{\mathrm{a}}^{\mathrm{x}} \mathrm{f(t)dt} = \mathrm{F(x)} - \mathrm{F(a)},\ \mathrm{a} \leqslant \mathrm{x} \leqslant \mathrm{b}.$$

To prove this we use the following result of the differential calculus. If $\phi'(x)=0$ in the interval $a\leqslant x\leqslant b$, $\phi(x)$ is constant and equal to $\phi(a)$ in this interval. Now consider

$$\frac{d}{dx}\left[\int_a^x f(t)dt - F(x)\right].$$

This is clearly zero and so

$$\int_a^x f(t)dt - F(x) = -F(a).$$

CHAPTER VI

INFINITE INTEGRALS

§ 32. In the previous chapter the integral of a function was defined when the function was bounded in the range of integration and when both limits of integration were finite numbers. In this chapter it is shown that a meaning can be given to the integral in certain cases when the function is infinite for some values of the variable in the range of integration and when the range of integration is infinite. In such cases the integral is called an **infinite integral**. We begin by discussing the case where the range of integration is infinite.

Let us suppose that the integral $\int_a^b f(x)dx$ exists for any value of b greater than a. If

$$\lim_{b \to \infty} \int_a^b f(x)dx = L,$$

where L is finite, this limit is called the integral of $f(x)$ from a to ∞, is written

$$\int_a^\infty f(x)dx,$$

and the integral is said to **converge**. If $F(x) = \int_a^x f(t)dt$, then $\int_a^\infty f(x)dx = \lim_{x \to \infty} F(x)$.

If $\lim_{b \to \infty} \int_a^b f(x)dx = \pm\infty$, the integral $\int_a^\infty f(x)dx$ is said to **diverge**. If as $b \to \infty$, the integral does not tend to a limit but is bounded, the integral is said to **oscillate finitely**. It should be noted that $\int_a^\infty f(x)dx$ is really a repeated limit, since $\int_a^b f(x)dx$ is itself the limit of a sum and the infinite integral is the limit of this limit for b tending to infinity.

It is clear that if we can find an indefinite integral for $f(x)$, *i.e.* if we can integrate $f(x)$ by the methods of Chapter II, we can at once test whether or not $\int_a^\infty f(x)dx$ converges. For example, if $a>0$,

$$\int_a^b \frac{dx}{x^2} = \frac{1}{a} - \frac{1}{b}, \text{ so that } \int_a^\infty \frac{dx}{x^2} = \frac{1}{a}.$$

Similarly we define $\int_{-\infty}^a f(x)dx$ as

$$\lim_{b \to -\infty} \int_b^a f(x)dx.$$

We define $\int_{-\infty}^\infty f(x)dx$ as

$$\lim_{b \to -\infty} \int_b^a f(x)dx + \lim_{c \to \infty} \int_a^c f(x)dx,$$

when both these limits exist. It should be noted that b must tend to $-\infty$ and c to ∞ independently. It is easy to see that in this definition a may be any finite number, for, if $F(x)$ is any indefinite integral of $f(x)$

$$\lim_{b \to -\infty} \int_b^a f(x)dx + \lim_{c \to \infty} \int_a^c f(x)dx$$
$$= F(a) - \lim_{b \to -\infty} F(b) + \lim_{c \to \infty} F(c) - F(a)$$
$$= -\lim_{b \to -\infty} F(b) + \lim_{c \to \infty} F(c).$$

§ 33. **Theorem**

A necessary and sufficient condition for the convergence of $\int_a^\infty f(x)dx$ *is that, given* ϵ, *we can find* x_0 *such that*

$$\left| \int_b^c f(x)dx \right| < \epsilon,$$

where b *and* c *are any numbers greater than* x_0.

If the integral converges to L, given any ϵ, we can find x_0 such that

$$\left| \int_a^k f(x)dx - L \right| < \frac{\epsilon}{2},$$

where k is any number greater than x_0. Hence, if b and c are each greater than x_0, $\left| \int_b^c f(x)dx \right| < \epsilon$. This proves the necessity of the condition.

To prove sufficiency is more difficult. Let $F(x) = \int_a^x f(t)dt$, so that we wish to show that $F(x)$ tends to a definite number as $x \to \infty$. We first show that $F(x)$ is bounded. Since for $b > x_0$, $c > x_0$,

$$|F(c) - F(b)| < \epsilon,$$

it follows that

$$F(b) - \epsilon < F(c) < F(b) + \epsilon.$$

Let us take a fixed value for b; then this inequality holds for every c greater than x_0. Hence $F(x)$ is bounded. Let K be the lower bound of all numbers which do not fall below $F(x)$ for $x > x_0$. This bound exists since all such numbers are greater than or equal to the lower bound of $F(x)$. Let L be the upper bound of all numbers which do not exceed $F(x)$ for $x > x_0$. The theorem will be proved if we show that $K = L$. Clearly $L \leqslant K$. Let us suppose that $L<K$; then no matter how small η is we can find values x_1, x_2 each greater than x_0 such that

$$F(x_1)<L+\eta, \quad F(x_2)>K-\eta.$$

Thus

$$F(x_2)-F(x_1)>K-L-2\eta>(K-L)/2,$$

if η is small enough. This contradicts the hypothesis.

If $f(x)$ is positive and if $\int_a^x f(t)dt<K$ for all values of x greater than a, then $\int_a^\infty f(x)dx$ converges. This follows at once since $\int_a^x f(t)dt$ is monotone increasing and bounded above.

We can deduce from this result that if $\phi(x)$, $\psi(x)$ are positive and $\phi(x)\leqslant\psi(x)$ for $x>x_0$, $\int_a^\infty \phi(x)dx$ converges if $\int_a^\infty \psi(x)dx$ converges. For example,

$\int_a^\infty \frac{\log x}{x^n}dx$, where $a>1$, $n\geqslant 2$, converges, since

$$\int_a^\infty \frac{\log x}{x^n}dx\leqslant\int_a^\infty \frac{\log x}{x^2}dx=\frac{\log a}{a}+\frac{1}{a}.$$

Ex. 1. Show that $\int_a^\infty e^{-x}x^{n-1}dx$, where $a>0$, converges for all values of n.

If $x>0$, $e^x>x^p/p\,!$, where p is any positive integer; hence $e^{-x}<p\,!/x^p$ and $e^{-x}x^{n-1}<p\,!/x^{p-n+1}$. Therefore if $0<b<c$,

$$\int_b^c e^{-x}x^{n-1}dx<p\,!\int_b^c \frac{dx}{x^{p-n+1}}.$$

The result follows when we choose p a positive integer greater than n.

Ex. 2. Show that $\int_0^\infty \frac{\sin x}{x}\, dx$ converges.

In any interval $0<x\leqslant k$, $\frac{\sin x}{x}$ is continuous and $\lim_{\epsilon\to 0} \frac{\sin \epsilon}{\epsilon} = 1$; hence, by § 30, $\int_0^k \frac{\sin x}{x}\, dx$ exists. Now if $0<b<c$,

$$\int_b^c \frac{\sin x}{x}\, dx = \left[-\frac{\cos x}{x}\right]_b^c - \int_b^c \frac{\cos x}{x^2}\, dx;$$

thus

$$\left|\int_b^c \frac{\sin x}{x}\, dx\right| < \frac{1}{b} + \frac{1}{c} + \int_b^c \frac{dx}{x^2} = \frac{2}{b}.$$

It follows at once that the integral converges.

§ 34. Absolute Convergence

If the integral $\int_a^\infty |f(x)|dx$ is convergent, the integral $\int_a^\infty f(x)dx$ is said to be **absolutely convergent**. An integral which is convergent but not absolutely convergent is said to be **conditionally convergent**. We now show that an absolutely convergent integral is convergent. We have

$$\int_a^b f(x)dx = \tfrac{1}{2}\int_a^b \{|f(x)|+f(x)\}dx - \tfrac{1}{2}\int_a^b \{|f(x)|-f(x)\}dx.$$

As $b\to\infty$ each integral on the right is convergent since the integrands are in absolute value less than $2|f(x)|$.

Ex. 1. Show that if $f(x)$ is bounded $\int_a^\infty \frac{f(x)}{x^n}\, dx$ converges absolutely, where $a>0$, $n>1$.

This follows at once since

$$\int_a^b \left|\frac{f(x)}{x^n}\right| dx \leqslant M \int_a^b \frac{dx}{x^n},\ (b>a),$$

where M is the upper bound of $|f(x)|$, and the second integral converges.

Ex. 2. Show that $\int_0^\infty \frac{\sin x}{x}\,dx$ is conditionally convergent.

We have already shown that the integral is convergent (§ 33, Ex. 2) and we have now to show that $\int_0^\infty \left|\frac{\sin x}{x}\right| dx$ is not convergent. Let us consider $\int_0^{n\pi} \left|\frac{\sin x}{x}\right| dx$, where n is a positive integer; then

$$\int_0^{n\pi} \left|\frac{\sin x}{x}\right| dx =$$

$$\int_0^{\pi} \frac{\sin x}{x}\,dx - \int_\pi^{2\pi} \frac{\sin x}{x}\,dx + \dots + (-1)^{n-1}\int_{(n-1)\pi}^{n\pi} \frac{\sin x}{x}\,dx$$

$$= \int_0^\pi \sin x \left[\frac{1}{x} + \frac{1}{x+\pi} + \dots + \frac{1}{x+(n-1)\pi}\right] dx$$

$$> \left[\frac{1}{\pi} + \frac{1}{2\pi} + \dots + \frac{1}{n\pi}\right] \int_0^\pi \sin x\,dx$$

$$= \frac{2}{\pi}\left[1 + \frac{1}{2} + \dots + \frac{1}{n}\right].$$

Hence as $n \to \infty$, $\int_0^{n\pi} \left|\frac{\sin x}{x}\right| dx \to \infty$.

§ 35. Infinite Integrand

The second type of infinite integral is one in which the integrand becomes infinite at a finite number of points in the range of integration. Let us take the case of $\int_b^a f(x)dx$, where $f(x) \to \infty$ as $x \to a$. Under the Riemann definition this has no meaning since it was assumed that $f(x)$ is bounded in the closed interval $a \leqslant x \leqslant b$. However, if

$$\lim_{\epsilon \to 0} \int_{a+\epsilon}^b f(x)dx$$

exists and is finite, this limit is called the infinite integral $\int_a^b f(x)dx$. The integral is said to be **convergent**.

Similarly, if $f(x) \to \infty$ as $x \to b$, we define $\int_a^b f(x)dx$ as

$$\lim_{\epsilon \to 0} \int_a^{b-\epsilon} f(x)dx,$$

f this limit exists. If $f(x) \to \infty$ as $x \to a$ and as $x \to b$, we say that $\int_a^b f(x)dx$ converges to

$$\lim_{\epsilon \to 0} \int_{a+\epsilon}^{c} f(x)dx + \lim_{\epsilon' \to 0} \int_c^{b-\epsilon'} f(x)dx,$$

if this limit exists, where ϵ and ϵ' tend to zero independently and c is any number between a and b. It may happen that $f(x) \to \infty$ as $x \to \xi$, where $a < \xi < b$; in that case $\int_a^b f(x)dx$ is said to converge to the sum of

$$\int_a^{\xi} f(x)dx + \int_{\xi}^{b} f(x)dx,$$

if both these integrals converge. This definition can obviously be extended to a finite number of infinities in the interval.

The following theorem is analogous to that of § 33. *If* f(x) *tends to infinity as* x→a, *a necessary and sufficient condition for the convergence of* $\int_a^b f(x)dx$ *is that, given* ϵ, *we can find* x_0 *such that*

$$\left| \int_h^k f(x)dx \right| < \epsilon,$$

where h, k *are any two numbers such that* $a < h < k < x_0 < b$.

The proof is similar to that of § 33.

If the integral converges, then, given ϵ, we can find x_0 such that

$$\left|\int_c^b f(x)dx - L\right| < \frac{\epsilon}{2},$$

where c is any number between a and x_0. Hence if h and k are any two such numbers,

$$\left|\int_h^k f(x)dx\right| < \epsilon.$$

The sufficiency proof follows exactly as in the previous case, taking $F(x) = \int_x^b f(t)dt$ and showing that $F(x)$ tends to a definite limit as $x \to a$ from above.

The following theorem is of great assistance in testing certain integrals for convergence. Let $f(x) = \phi(x) \cdot \psi(x)$, where, as $x \to a$, $\phi(x) \to K$, a finite non-zero limit, and $\psi(x) \to \infty$. The theorem states that if $\int_a^b \psi(x)dx$ converges (or diverges), so does $\int_a^b f(x)dx$. A shorthand way of expressing the result is to say that near $x = a$, the function $f(x)$ behaves like $\psi(x)$.

The proof for convergence is as follows. We may assume K to be positive (otherwise consider $-\phi(x)$). Since $\phi(x) \to K$ as $x \to a$, given ϵ, we can find x_0 such that $|K - \phi(x)| < \epsilon$, when $a < x < x_0$. Let h, k be any two numbers in the interval $a < x < x_0$; then

$$\left|\int_h^k \phi(x)\psi(x)dx\right| < (K+\epsilon)\left|\int_h^k \psi(x)dx\right|,$$

and the result follows since $\int_a^b \psi(x)dx$ converges.

The proof for divergence is similar.

A corresponding theorem holds when the range of integration is infinite. If $\phi(x) \to K$, a finite non-zero limit, as $x \to \infty$, and if $\int_a^\infty \psi(x)dx$ converges (or diverges), then so does $\int_a^\infty \phi(x)\psi(x)dx$. The proof is similar to the previous one.

Ex. 1. Show that $\int_0^k e^{-x}x^{n-1}dx$ converges when $n>0$.

Near $x = 0$, $e^{-x}x^{n-1}$ behaves like x^{n-1}, and hence the integral converges when $n>0$.

Ex. 2. Show that $\int_0^1 x^{m-1}(1-x)^{n-1}dx$ converges when $m>0$, $n>0$.

Near $x = 0$, the integrand behaves like x^{m-1}, so that for convergence we require $m>0$.

Near $x = 1$, the integrand behaves like $(1-x)^{n-1}$, so that for convergence we require $n>0$.

Ex. 3. Show that $\int_0^\infty \frac{x^{\alpha-1}}{1+x^\beta}dx$ is convergent only if α lies between 0 and β.

We shall discuss separately the cases where $\beta>0$, $\beta<0$, $\beta=0$.

(i) $\beta>0$. Near $x = 0$, the integrand behaves like $x^{\alpha-1}$ and near $x = \infty$, like $x^{\alpha-\beta-1}$. Hence for convergence we require $\alpha>0$ and $\alpha-\beta<0$; *i.e.* $0<\alpha<\beta$.

(ii) $\beta<0$. Near $x = 0$, the integrand behaves like $x^{\alpha-\beta-1}$ and near $x = \infty$, like $x^{\alpha-1}$. Hence for convergence we require $\alpha-\beta>0$ and $\alpha<0$; *i.e.* $\beta<\alpha<0$.

(iii) $\beta=0$. The integrand is $\frac{1}{2}x^{\alpha-1}$ and clearly the integral does not converge.

§ 36. (*a*) $\int_0^\infty \frac{\sin x}{x}dx = \frac{\pi}{2}$.

In the proof of this result we use the series *

$$\sum_{k=0}^{\infty}(-1)^k\left[\frac{1}{k\pi+\theta}+\frac{1}{(k+1)\pi-\theta}\right]$$

* See MacRobert and Arthur, *Trigonometry*, p. 426.

which in any closed interval (a, b) where $0<a<b<\pi$ converges uniformly to $1/\sin\theta$. We consider the integral

$$\int_0^{(n+1)\pi} \frac{\sin x}{x}\,dx = \sum_{k=0}^{n}\int_{k\pi}^{(k+1)\pi}\frac{\sin x}{x}\,dx = \sum_{k=0}^{n}(-1)^k\int_0^{\pi}\frac{\sin x}{k\pi+x}\,dx$$

$$= \int_0^{\frac{\pi}{2}} \sin x\left[\sum_{k=0}^{n}(-1)^k\left(\frac{1}{k\pi+x}+\frac{1}{(k+1)\pi-x}\right)\right]dx$$

$$= \int_0^{\epsilon} \dots\,dx + \int_{\epsilon}^{\frac{\pi}{2}}\dots\,dx, \text{ where } 0<\epsilon<\frac{\pi}{2}.$$

The first integral is less than $M\epsilon$, where M is the upper bound of the integrand. Since the integrand in the second integral tends to 1 uniformly with respect x in the interval $\epsilon\leqslant x\leqslant\pi/2$ as $n\to\infty$, the second integral tends to the value $\pi/2-\epsilon$ as $n\to\infty$. In the first integral M remains finite as $n\to\infty$. Since ϵ is arbitrary, we have proved that

$$\int_0^{\infty}\frac{\sin x}{x}\,dx = \frac{\pi}{2}.$$

(b) $\displaystyle\int_0^{\infty}\frac{\mathbf{x}^{\mathbf{p}-1}}{1+\mathbf{x}}\,\mathbf{dx} = \frac{\pi}{\sin \mathbf{p}\pi}$, **where** $\mathbf{0<p<1}$.

Since the integrand near $x=0$ behaves like x^{p-1}, and for large values of x behaves like x^{p-2}, the integral converges. Now

$$\int_0^{\infty}\frac{x^{p-1}}{1+x}dx = \int_0^1\frac{x^{p-1}}{1+x}\,dx+\int_0^1\frac{y^{-p}}{1+y}\,dy, \text{ where } y=1/x,$$

$$=\int_0^1 (x^{p-1}+x^{-p})\left[1-x+x^2-\dots+(-1)^n x^n+(-1)^{n+1}\frac{x^{n+1}}{1+x}\right]dx$$

$$=\sum_{k=0}^{n}(-1)^k\left(\frac{1}{k+p}+\frac{1}{k+1-p}\right)+R_n,$$

where

$$|R_n| < \int_0^1 (x^{p-1}+x^{-p})x^{n+1}dx = \frac{1}{n+p+1} + \frac{1}{n+2-p}.$$

In the above series for $1/\sin\theta$, let $\theta = p\pi$, and we see that

$$\sum_{k=0}^{\infty} (-1)^k \left(\frac{1}{k+p} + \frac{1}{k+1-p}\right) = \frac{\pi}{\sin p\pi}.$$

Hence the result follows when $n \to \infty$.

§ 37. Gamma and Beta Functions

We have already shown that the integral

$$\int_0^\infty e^{-x}x^{n-1}dx$$

converges if $n>0$, (§ 33, Ex. 1, § 35, Ex. 1). This integral is a function of n and is called the **Gamma Function**, $\Gamma(\mathbf{n})$. We have also shown that the integral

$$\int_0^1 x^{m-1}(1-x)^{n-1}dx$$

converges if $m>0$, $n>0$ (§ 35, Ex. 2). This integral is a function of m and n and is called the **Beta Function**, $\mathbf{B(m, n)}$. These functions, which we shall show to be related, are very important in pure and applied mathematics and we shall investigate some of their properties.

(1) $\Gamma(1) = 1$,

for $\Gamma(1) = \int_0^\infty e^{-x}dx = 1$.

(2) $\Gamma(n) = (n-1)\Gamma(n-1)$, if $n-1>0$,

for

$$\Gamma(n) = \int_0^\infty e^{-x}x^{n-1}dx = \left[-e^{-x}x^{n-1}\right]_0^\infty + (n-1)\int_0^\infty e^{-x}x^{n-2}dx.$$

(3) If n is a positive integer $\Gamma(n) = (n-1)!$.

This follows at once from (2), since

$$\Gamma(n) = (n-1)\Gamma(n-1) = (n-1)(n-2)\Gamma(n-2)$$
$$= (n-1)!\ \Gamma(1) = (n-1)!.$$

(4) $$B(m, n) = 2\int_0^{\frac{\pi}{2}} \sin^{2m-1}\theta \cos^{2n-1}\theta\, d\theta,$$

for, in the integral which defines $B(m, n)$ put $x = \sin^2\theta$.

(5) $B(m, n) = B(n, m)$,

since $\int_0^1 f(x)dx = \int_0^1 f(1-x)dx$, (p. 14).

(6) $$B(m, n) = \frac{(m-1)(n-1)}{(m+n-1)(m+n-2)} B(m-1, n-1),$$

if $m-1>0$, $n-1>0$.

By the formula on p. 21.

$$B(m, n) = 2\frac{2n-2}{2m+2n-2}\int_0^{\frac{\pi}{2}} \sin^{2m-1}\theta \cos^{2n-3}\theta\, d\theta$$

$$= 2\frac{n-1}{m+n-1}\int_0^{\frac{\pi}{2}} \cos^{2m-1}\theta \sin^{2n-3}\theta\, d\theta$$

$$= 2\frac{(m-1)(n-1)}{(m+n-1)(m+n-2)}\int_0^{\frac{\pi}{2}} \sin^{2n-3}\theta \cos^{2m-3}\theta\, d\theta$$

$$= \frac{(m-1)(n-1)}{(m+n-1)(m+n-2)} B(m-1, n-1).$$

(7) If m, n are positive integers

$$B(m, n) = \frac{(m-1)!(n-1)!}{(m+n-1)!}.$$

This follows from (6) since $B(1, 1) = 1$.

(8) $B(\frac{1}{2}, \frac{1}{2}) = \pi$.

This follows at once from (4).

(9) $B(m, n) = \int_0^\infty \frac{x^{m-1}}{(1+x)^{m+n}}\, dx = \int_0^\infty \frac{x^{n-1}}{(1+x)^{m+n}}\, dx.$

In $\int_0^1 x^{m-1}(1-x)^{n-1}dx$, let $x = \frac{1}{1+y}$, so that the integral becomes

$$\int_0^\infty \left(\frac{1}{1+y}\right)^{m-1} \left(\frac{y}{1+y}\right)^{n-1} \frac{dy}{(1+y)^2} = \int_0^\infty \frac{y^{n-1}}{(1+y)^{m+n}}\, dy,$$

and this is equal to the first integral in (9), by (5).

(10) $B(m, n) = \int_0^1 \frac{x^{m-1}+x^{n-1}}{(1+x)^{m+n}}\, dx.$

We use (9) and write

$$B(m, n) = \int_0^1 \frac{x^{n-1}}{(1+x)^{m+n}}\, dx + \int_1^\infty \frac{x^{n-1}}{(1+x)^{m+n}}\, dx;$$

the second integral becomes on letting $y = \frac{1}{x}$

$$\int_0^1 \frac{y^{m-1}}{(1+y)^{m+n}} dy.$$

§ 38. Relation between the Gamma and Beta Functions

$$\mathbf{B(m, n) = \frac{\Gamma(m)\Gamma(n)}{\Gamma(m+n)}}.$$

Let $U = 2\int_0^a e^{-x^2} x^{2m-1} dx$, $V = 2\int_0^a e^{-y^2} y^{2n-1} dy$,

so that

$$\lim_{a \to \infty} U = \Gamma(m), \lim_{a \to \infty} V = \Gamma(n).$$

Now

$$UV = 4\int_0^a dx \int_0^a e^{-(x^2+y^2)} x^{2m-1} y^{2n-1} dy$$

$$= 4\iint e^{-r^2} r^{2m+2n-1} \cos^{2m-1}\theta \sin^{2n-1}\theta \, dr\, d\theta$$

$$= \iint f(r, \theta) dr\, d\theta, \text{ say,}$$

over the square bounded by the lines $x = 0, a$; $y = 0, a$. Since $f(r, \theta)$ is positive UV lies between I_1 and I_2 where I_1, I_2 are the values of $\iint f(r, \theta) dr\, d\theta$ over the first quadrants of the circles $x^2+y^2 = a^2$, $x^2+y^2 = 2a^2$; *i.e.*

$$I_1 = 4\int_0^{\frac{\pi}{2}} \cos^{2m-1}\theta \sin^{2n-1}\theta \, d\theta \int_0^a e^{-r^2} r^{2m+2n-1} \, dr,$$

$$I_2 = 4\int_0^{\frac{\pi}{2}} \cos^{2m-1}\theta \sin^{2n-1}\theta \, d\theta \int_0^{a\sqrt{2}} e^{-r^2} r^{2m+2n-1} \, dr.$$

As $a \to \infty$, I_1 and I_2 each tend to $\mathrm{B}(m, n)\Gamma(m+n)$ and UV tends to $\Gamma(m)\Gamma(n)$. Hence

$$\mathrm{B}(m, n) = \frac{\Gamma(m)\Gamma(n)}{\Gamma(m+n)}.$$

With the help of this result we can deduce more properties of the functions.

(1) $\Gamma(\frac{1}{2}) = \sqrt{\pi}$,

for $\mathrm{B}(\frac{1}{2}, \frac{1}{2}) = \Gamma(\frac{1}{2})\Gamma(\frac{1}{2})/\Gamma(1) = \pi$, and $\Gamma(\frac{1}{2})$ is clearly positive.

(2) $\Gamma(p)\Gamma(1-p) = \dfrac{\pi}{\sin p\pi}$, where $0<p<1$.

In § 36 (*b*) we showed that

$$\int_0^\infty \frac{x^{p-1}}{1+x} dx = \frac{\pi}{\sin p\pi}, \quad 0<p<1.$$

This integral is $\mathrm{B}(p, 1-p) = \Gamma(p)\Gamma(1-p)/\Gamma(1)$.

(3) $\Gamma(2p) = \dfrac{2^{2p-1}}{\sqrt{\pi}} \Gamma(p)\Gamma(p+\frac{1}{2})$.

For,

$$B(p, p) = 2\int_0^{\frac{\pi}{2}} \sin^{2p-1}\theta \cos^{2p-1}\theta \, d\theta = 2^{2-2p}\int_0^{\frac{\pi}{2}} (\sin 2\theta)^{2p-1} d\theta$$

$$= 2^{1-2p}\int_0^{\pi} (\sin u)^{2p-1}\, du = 2^{2-2p}\int_0^{\frac{\pi}{2}} (\sin u)^{2p-1}\, du$$

$$= 2^{1-2p}B(p, \tfrac{1}{2}),$$

and so

$$\frac{\Gamma(p)\Gamma(p)}{\Gamma(2p)} = 2^{1-2p}\frac{\Gamma(p)\Gamma(\frac{1}{2})}{\Gamma(p+\frac{1}{2})},$$

from which the result follows.

(4) $$\int_0^{\infty} e^{-x^2} dx = \frac{\sqrt{\pi}}{2},$$

for $$\int_0^{\infty} e^{-x^2} dx = \tfrac{1}{2}\int_0^{\infty} e^{-y} y^{-\frac{1}{2}} dy = \tfrac{1}{2}\Gamma(\tfrac{1}{2}) = \frac{\sqrt{\pi}}{2}.$$

Ex. 1. Show that

$$\int_0^a dx \int_0^{a-x} x^{m-1}y^{n-1}f(x+y)dy = B(m, n)\int_0^a f(u)u^{m+n-1}du,$$

where $m>0$, $n>0$ and the integral on the right exists.

We use the transformation $x+y=u$, $x=uv$ and formally obtain the above result. To prove the result rigorously we would require to show that the limits which are the repeated infinite integrals are equal. We *state* the theorem: if $f(x,y)$ is bounded and integrable over an area A' and if $\lim_{A'\to A}\iint f(x, y)dx\, dy$ exists, then $\lim_{B'\to B}\iint F(u, v)\left|\frac{\partial(x, y)}{\partial(u, v)}\right| du\, dv$ exists and is equal to the first limit, where $f[x(u, v), y(u, v)] \equiv F(u, v)$ and B', B are the areas in the (u, v) plane corresponding to A', A in the (x, y) plane.

Ex. 2. Show that

$$\int_0^a dx \int_0^{a-x} dy \int_0^{a-x-y} x^{l-1}y^{m-1}z^{n-1}f(x+y+z)dz$$

$$= \frac{\Gamma(l)\Gamma(m)\Gamma(n)}{\Gamma(l+m+n)}\int_0^a u^{l+m+n-1}f(u)du,$$

where $l>0$, $m>0$, $n>0$ and the integral on the right converges.

(Let $x+y+z = u$, $x+y = uv$, $x = uvw$.)

Ex. 3. A similar transformation is

$$\int_0^\infty dx \int_0^x f(x-y)g(y)dy = \int_0^\infty f(u)du \int_0^\infty g(v)dv,$$

obtained by putting $x = u+v$, $y = v$.

§ 39. Uniform Convergence of an Integral

Let $f(x,y)$ be a function which is continuous with respect to the pair of variables (x, y) in the closed rectangle $a \leqslant x \leqslant b$, $\alpha \leqslant y \leqslant \beta$ [§ 27, (6)]. Then for any value of x in the interval $a \leqslant x \leqslant b$ the integral

$$\int_\alpha^\beta f(x, y)dy$$

exists, since $f(x,y)$ is clearly a continuous function of y in the interval $\alpha \leqslant y \leqslant \beta$. The integral is a function of x. Let us now suppose that the integral

$$\int_\alpha^\infty f(x, y)dy$$

exists for each value of x in the interval $a < x < b$; *i.e.* given any ϵ, we can find y_0 such that

$$\left| \int_\alpha^k f(x, y)dy - \phi(x) \right| < \epsilon,$$

where k is any number greater than y_0. In general y_0 depends on the particular value of x in the interval $a \leqslant x \leqslant b$, but if we can find y_0 the same for every x in the interval, the integral $\int_\alpha^\infty f(x, y)dy$ is said **to converge to $\phi(x)$ uniformly with respect to x in the interval** $a \leqslant x \leqslant b$. We now prove the following theorem.

If f(x, y) *is a continuous function of the pair of variables* (x, y) *in the closed rectangle* $a \leqslant x \leqslant b$, $\alpha \leqslant y \leqslant \beta$ *for all values of* β *greater than* α, *and if the integral* $\phi(x) = \int_\alpha^\infty f(x, y)dy$ *converges uniformly with respect to* x *in the interval* $a \leqslant x \leqslant b$, *then* $\phi(x)$ *is a continuous function of* x *in this interval.*

If x, $x+h$ lie in the closed interval (a, b),

$$\phi(x+h)-\phi(x)=\int_a^\infty [f(x+h, y)-f(x, y)]dy$$

$$=\int_a^{y_0}[f(x+h, y)-f(x, y)]dy+\int_{y_0}^\infty f(x+h, y)dy-\int_{y_0}^\infty f(x, y)dy.$$

Now, given ϵ, we can choose y_0 so that each of the last two integrals is numerically less than ϵ, and we can then find η such that the first integral is numerically less than ϵ if $|h|<\eta$; *i.e.*

$$|\phi(x+h)-\phi(x)|<3\epsilon, \text{ if } |h|<\eta.$$

This proves the theorem.

The following theorem, which is proved in the same manner as that in § 33, is important.

A necessary and sufficient condition that the integral $\int_a^\infty f(x, y)dy$ *should converge uniformly with respect to* x *in the interval* $a \leqslant x \leqslant b$ *is that, given* ϵ, *we can find* y_0 *such that*

$$\left|\int_h^k f(x, y)dy\right|<\epsilon,$$

where h, k *are any numbers greater than* y_0, *and* y_0 *is the same for every* x *in the interval.*

§ 40. Theorem

If f(x, y) *is continuous with respect to the pair of variables* (x, y) *in the closed rectangle* $a \leqslant x \leqslant b$, $\alpha \leqslant y \leqslant \beta$, *for all values of* β *greater than* α, *and if the integral* $\int_\alpha^\infty f(x, y)dy$ *is uniformly convergent in the interval* $a \leqslant x \leqslant b$, *then*

$$\int_a^x dx\int_\alpha^\infty f(x, y)dy=\int_\alpha^\infty dy\int_a^x f(x, y)dx, \quad a\leqslant x\leqslant b.$$

The repeated integral $\int_a^x dx \int_x^\infty f(x,y)dy$ exists since $\int_a^\infty f(x, y)dy$ is a continuous function of x in $a \leqslant x \leqslant b$. Now

$$\int_a^\beta dy \int_a^x f(x, y)dx = \int_a^x dx \int_a^\beta f(x, y)dy$$

$$= \int_a^x dx \int_a^\infty f(x, y)dy - \int_a^x dx \int_\beta^\infty f(x, y)dy.$$

Given ϵ, we can find y_0 such that

$$\left| \int_\beta^\infty f(x, y)dy \right| < \epsilon, \text{ if } \beta > y_0,\ a \leqslant x \leqslant b.$$

Hence $$\left| \int_a^x dx \int_\beta^\infty f(x, y)dy \right| < \epsilon(b-a), \text{ so that}$$

$$\left| \int_a^\beta dy \int_a^x f(x, y)dx - \int_a^x dx \int_a^\infty f(x, y)dy \right| < \epsilon(b-a), \text{ if } \beta > y_0.$$

This proves the theorem.

As an example let us take $\int_a^b dx \int_0^\infty e^{-xy}dy$ where $b>a>0$.

Since $\int_0^\infty e^{-xy}dy$ converges uniformly for $a \leqslant x \leqslant b$ to $1/x$, the repeated integral is by the theorem equal to

$$\int_0^\infty dy \int_a^b e^{-xy}dx = \int_0^\infty \frac{e^{-ay}-e^{-by}}{y} dy.$$

It will be seen from this example that the above theorem gives us a method of evaluating certain integrals.

Ex. If $a>0$, $b>0$, show that

$$\int_0^\infty \frac{e^{-ax^2} - e^{-bx^2}}{x^2} dx = \sqrt{\pi}(\sqrt{b}-\sqrt{a}).$$

§ 41. Differentiation under the Integral Sign

If f(x, y), $\frac{\partial f}{\partial x}$ *are continuous with respect to the pair of variables* (x,y) *in the closed rectangle* $a \leqslant x \leqslant b$, $\alpha \leqslant y \leqslant \beta$ *for all values of* β *greater than* α, *and if* $\int_a^\infty f(x,y)dy$ *is convergent and* $\int_a^\infty \frac{\partial f}{\partial x}\,dy$ *is uniformly convergent in the interval* $a \leqslant x \leqslant b$, *then*

$$\frac{d}{dx}\int_a^\infty f(x,y)dy = \int_a^\infty \frac{\partial f}{\partial x}\,dy,\ a \leqslant x \leqslant b.$$

By the last paragraph

$$\int_a^x dx \int_a^\infty \frac{\partial f}{\partial x}\,dy = \int_a^\infty dy \int_a^x \frac{\partial f}{\partial x}\,dx$$

$$= \int_a^\infty f(x, y)dy - \int_a^\infty f(a, y)dy.$$

Since the derivative of the left-hand side exists, so does that of the right-hand side and the two are equal ; *i.e.*

$$\int_a^\infty \frac{\partial f}{\partial x}\,dy = \frac{d}{dx}\int_a^\infty f(x, y)dy.$$

Ex. Show that $\int_0^\infty e^{-a^2x^2} \cos 2bx\,dx = \frac{\sqrt{\pi}}{2a} e^{-\frac{b^2}{a^2}}$, when $a > 0$.

For all values of b

$$\left|\int_h^k e^{-a^2x^2} \cos 2bx\,dx\right| \leqslant \left|\int_h^k e^{-a^2x^2}dx\right|,$$

so that the integral is convergent. Also

$$\left|\int_h^k -2x\,e^{-a^2x^2} \sin 2bx\,dx\right| \leqslant \left|\int_h^k 2x\,e^{-a^2x^2}dx\right|$$

for all values of b; hence

$$\frac{d}{db}\int_0^\infty e^{-a^2x^2}\cos 2bx\,dx = \int_0^\infty -2x\,e^{-a^2x^2}\sin 2bx\,dx$$

$$= \int_0^\infty -\frac{2b}{a^2}e^{-a^2x^2}\cos 2bx dx,$$

on integration by parts. Thus, if I denotes the integral,

$$\frac{dI}{db}+\frac{2b}{a^2}I = 0,$$

for all values of b; *i.e.* $I = Ke^{-\frac{b^2}{a^2}}$, where K is a function of a. Now when $b = 0$,

$$I = \int_0^\infty e^{-a^2x^2}dx = \frac{\sqrt{\pi}}{2a}, \quad [\S\ 38, (4)];$$

hence $K = \dfrac{\sqrt{\pi}}{2a}$. This proves the result.

Examples IV.

1. Examine the convergence of the integrals

(i) $\displaystyle\int_0^1 \frac{x^b-x^a}{\log x}dx$, (ii) $\displaystyle\int_0^\infty x^{-h}\sin(x^{1-k})dx,\ h>k>0,$

(iii) $\displaystyle\int_0^1 \frac{x^x}{(1-x)^\beta}\log\left(\frac{1}{x}\right)dx$, (iv) $\displaystyle\int_0^\infty \frac{\sin^3 x}{x^\alpha}\,dx,$

(v) $\displaystyle\int_0^1 x^{n-1}\log\Gamma(x)dx$, (vi) $\displaystyle\int_a^\infty x^m(x^2-a^2)^n dx,\ a>0.$

2. Show that, if $a<-1$, the integral $\displaystyle\int_0^\infty \tan^{-1}(x^a)dx$ converges and that its value is

$$\frac{1}{2}\,\frac{\pi}{\sin\frac{(a+1)\pi}{2a}}.$$

3. Prove that

(i) $\displaystyle\int_a^b \frac{x\,dx}{(x-a)^{\frac{1}{3}}(b-x)^{\frac{2}{3}}} = \frac{2\pi}{3\sqrt{3}}(a+2b),$

(ii) $$\int_0^1 \frac{x^{m-1}(1-x)^{n-1}}{(x+a)^{m+n}}\,dx = \frac{B(m,\,n)}{(1+a)^m a^n},\ a>0,\ m>0,\ n>0.$$

4. Show that

$$\iint x^{2m-1}y^{2n-1}dx\,dy = \frac{B(m,\,n)}{4(m+n)}\,a^{2(m+n)},\ m>0,\ n>0,$$

the field of integration being such that x, y are positive and $x^2+y^2 \leqslant a^2$.

5. Show that, if $l>0$, $m>0$, $n>0$,

$$\iiint x^{l-1}y^{m-1}z^{n-1}dx\,dy\,dz = \frac{1}{8}\,a^l b^m c^n\,\frac{\Gamma\left(\frac{l}{2}\right)\Gamma\left(\frac{m}{2}\right)\Gamma\left(\frac{n}{2}\right)}{\Gamma\left(\frac{l+m+n+2}{2}\right)},$$

where the integral is taken through that part of the ellipsoid $x^2/a^2+y^2/b^2+z^2/c^2 = 1$ which lies in the positive octant.

6. Show that

$$\int_0^1 dx\int_0^{1-x} dy\int_0^{1-x-y} \frac{x^{l-1}y^{m-1}z^{n-1}}{(x+y+z)^{l+m+n-1}}\,dz = \frac{\Gamma(l)\Gamma(m)\Gamma(n)}{\Gamma(l+m+n)},$$

where $l>0$, $m>0$, $n>0$.

7. Prove that

(i) $$\int_0^{\frac{\pi}{2}} \frac{\log\,(1-a^2\sin^2 x)}{\sin x}\,dx = -(\sin^{-1} a)^2,\ 0\leqslant a<1,$$

(ii) $$\int_0^\infty \frac{\operatorname{sech} ax - \operatorname{sech} bx}{x}\,dx = \log\frac{b}{a},\ a>0,\ b>0,$$

(iii) $$\int_0^\infty \frac{\tan^{-1} ax\,.\,\tan^{-1} 2ax}{x^2}\,dx = \frac{\pi a}{2}\log\frac{27}{4},\ a\geqslant 0.$$

8. Show that

$$\int_0^\infty \frac{\log x}{(a+x)^n}\,dx = \frac{1}{(n-1)a^{n-1}}\left[\log a - \sum_{r=1}^{n-2}\frac{1}{r}\right],$$

where $a>0$ and n is an integer greater than 1.

9. Show that

(i) $$\int_0^\infty \frac{\cosh \lambda x}{\cosh x}\, dx = \frac{\pi}{2 \cos (\frac{1}{2}\lambda\pi)}, \quad -1<\lambda<1,$$

(ii) $$\int_0^\infty \frac{\sinh \lambda x}{x \cosh x}\, dx = \tfrac{1}{2} \log \left[\frac{1+\sin (\frac{1}{2}\lambda\pi)}{1-\sin (\frac{1}{2}\lambda\pi)}\right], \quad -1<\lambda<1.$$

10. Prove that, if n is a positive integer,

$$\Gamma\left(\frac{1}{n}\right)\Gamma\left(\frac{2}{n}\right)\dots\Gamma\left(\frac{n-1}{n}\right) = \frac{(2\pi)^{\frac{n-1}{2}}}{\sqrt{(n)}}.$$

11. Show that

$$\lim_{n\to\infty} \frac{n^x \,.\, n!}{x(x+1)(x+2)\dots(x+n)} = \Gamma(x),$$

where $x>0$.

12. Show that

(i) $$\int_0^\pi \frac{\sin^{\frac{1}{2}} x\, dx}{(5+3 \cos x)^{\frac{3}{2}}} = \frac{\{\Gamma(\frac{3}{4})\}^2}{2\sqrt{(2\pi)}},$$

(ii) $$\int_0^{\frac{\pi}{2}} \frac{(\sin x)^{2m-1}(\cos x)^{2n-1}}{(a \cos^2 x+b \sin^2 x)^{m+n}}\, dx = \frac{\mathrm{B}(m, n)}{2a^n b^m}, \quad a>0,\ b>0,$$

(iii) $$\int_{-a}^{a} (a+x)^{m-1}(a-x)^{n-1}dx = (2a)^{m+n-1}\mathrm{B}(m, n),$$

where a, m, n are all greater than zero.

13. Prove that, if $0<n<1$,

$$\int_0^\infty e^{-y} \int_0^y \frac{x^{n-1}}{(y-x)^n}\, dx = \frac{\pi}{\sin n\pi}.$$

14. Show that

$$\int_{-\infty}^\infty \frac{\sin \pi x}{x(x-1)(x-2)\dots(x-n)} = (-1)^n \frac{2^n}{n!}\pi.$$

15. If $a^4 uy = x^5$, $a^4 vx = y^5$, show that

$$\frac{\partial(x, y)}{\partial(u, v)} = \frac{a^2}{24(uv)^{\frac{3}{4}}}.$$

Hence show that the area of a loop of the curve $x^6+y^6 = a^4xy$ is

$$a^2\{\Gamma(\tfrac{1}{4})\}^2/12\sqrt{\pi}.$$

16. Show that, if $0<\alpha<\pi$,

$$\int_0^\infty \frac{\sinh x\,dx}{(\cosh x+\cos\alpha\sinh x)^2} = \operatorname{cosec}^2\alpha(1-\alpha\cot\alpha).$$

17. Express in terms of Gamma Functions the volume V of the solid bounded by the surface whose equation is $x^4+y^4+a^2z^2 = a^4$, and show that if A is the area of the section of this solid by the plane $z = 0$, $2V = \pi aA$.

18. Show that, if $a>b>0$,

$$\int_0^{\frac{\pi}{2}} \frac{dx}{a^2-b^2\sin^2 x} = \frac{\pi}{2a(a^2-b^2)^{\frac{1}{2}}},$$

and deduce that

$$\int_0^{\frac{\pi}{2}} \frac{\cos^2 x\,dx}{(a^2-b^2\cos^2 x)^2} = \frac{\pi}{4a(a^2-b^2)^{\frac{3}{2}}}.$$

19. Show that

$$\int_0^{\frac{\pi}{2}} \frac{\tan^2 x\,dx}{(a^2+b^2\tan^2 x)^3} = \frac{\pi(3a+b)}{16a^3b(a+b)^3},\ a>0,\ b>0.$$

$$\left[\text{Evaluate first } \int_0^{\frac{\pi}{2}} \frac{dx}{a^2+b^2\tan^2 x}.\right]$$

20. Show that, if $m>0$ and $0<n<1$,

$$\iint \frac{x^{m-1}y^{n-1}}{(1-x-y)^n}\,dx\,dy = \frac{\pi}{m\sin n\pi},$$

where the field of integration is bounded by the coordinate axes and the line $x+y = 1$.

21. Show that the area of the part of the cone $z^2 = 2xy$ which lies within the cylinder $x^2+y^2 = 2ax$ is $2\pi a^2$.

CHAPTER VII

THE RIEMANN DOUBLE INTEGRAL

§ 42. In this chapter we return to the discussion of the Riemann integral. We begin by proving some further properties of the integral defined in Chapter V and then proceed to discuss a rigorous definition of the double integral. This will involve a treatment of the conditions that a curve must satisfy in order that it may possess a length.

§ 43. Change of Variable

We shall now justify the method of change of variable so extensively used in Chapter II. We begin by proving the following lemma :

If f(x), g(x) *are integrable over* (a, b), *so is* f(x)g(x).

Let m_1, M_1 ; m_2, M_2 ; m, M be the bounds of f, g, fg respectively in any sub-interval of (a, b) and let H, K be the upper bounds of $|f|$, $|g|$ in (a, b). Given any ϵ, we can find ξ, ζ, points of the sub-interval such that

$$f(\xi)g(\xi)>M-\epsilon\ ,\ f(\zeta)g(\zeta)<m+\epsilon.$$

Then

$$\begin{aligned} M-m &< f(\xi)g(\xi)-f(\zeta)g(\zeta)+2\epsilon \\ &= f(\xi)[g(\xi)-g(\zeta)]+g(\zeta)[f(\xi)-f(\zeta)]+2\epsilon \\ &< H(M_2-m_2)+K(M_1-m_1)+2\epsilon, \end{aligned}$$

and, since ϵ is arbitrary, it follows that

$$M-m\leqslant H(M_2-m_2)+K(M_1-m_1).$$

Hence fg is integrable.

We now prove the following theorem on change of variable.

If the integrals $\int_a^b f(x)dx$, $\int_c^d \phi'(t)dt$ *exist and if* $a = \phi(c)$, $b = \phi(d)$ *and* $\phi'(t) > 0$ [*or* $\phi'(t) < 0$] *in* (c, d), *then*

$$\int_a^b f(x)dx = \int_c^d f[\phi(t)]\phi'(t)dt.$$

We shall assume $\phi'(t) > 0$. The relation $x = \phi(t)$ defines t as $\psi(x)$, where $\psi(x)$ is a single-valued function of x, whose derivative $\psi'(x)$ exists and is greater than zero in (a, b). We first show that $f[\phi(t)]$ is integrable over the interval (c, d).

Let (t_r), $r = 0, 1, \ldots, n$, be points of division of (c, d) such that

$$c = t_0 < t_1 < \ldots < t_n = d,$$

and let us form the sum

$$\sum_{r=1}^{n} f[\phi(\tau_r)](t_r - t_{r-1}),$$

where τ_r belongs to the interval (t_{r-1}, t_r). Let $x_r = \phi(t_r)$, $x_{r-1} = \phi(t_{r-1})$; then for the function $f[\phi(t)]$ and for this method of dividing (c, d)

$$\mathbf{S} - \mathbf{s} = \Sigma(M_r - m_r)(t_r - t_{r-1}),$$

where M_r, m_r are the bounds of $f(x)$ in (x_{r-1}, x_r).

Now $$t_r - t_{r-1} = \psi'(\xi_r) \cdot (x_r - x_{r-1}),$$

where $x_{r-1} \leqslant \xi_r \leqslant x_r$, and so

$$\mathbf{S} - \mathbf{s} \leqslant K\Sigma(M_r - m_r)(x_r - x_{r-1}),$$

where K is the maximum value of $\psi'(x)$ in (a, b). Hence $f[\phi(t)]$ is integrable over (c, d). Since $\phi'(t)$ is integrable over (c, d), it follows from the lemma that $f[\phi(t)]\phi'(t)$ is integrable over this interval.

If ζ_r is any point of the interval (x_{r-1}, x_r), $\int_a^b f(x)dx$ is the number to which the expression

$$\sum_{r=1}^{n} f(\zeta_r) \,.\, (x_r - x_{r-1})$$

tends as the maximum of $x_r - x_{r-1}$ tends to zero. This expression is equal to

$$\sum_{r=1}^{n} f(\zeta_r)\phi'(\lambda_r) \,.\, (t_r - t_{r-1}),$$

where $t_{r-1} \leqslant \lambda_r \leqslant t_r$. Since ζ_r may be any point in (x_{r-1}, x_r), we may choose $\zeta_r = \phi(\lambda_r)$, and so $\int_a^b f(x)dx$ is the number to which the expression

$$\sum_{r=1}^{n} f[\phi(\lambda_r)]\phi'(\lambda_r) \,.\, (t_r - t_{r-1})$$

tends as each $t_r - t_{r-1}$ tends to zero. Since $\int_c^d f[\phi(t)]\phi'(t)dt$ has been proved to exist the result follows.

§ 44. Integration by Parts

If $F'(x) = f(x)$ *and if* $f(x)$, $g'(x)$ *are continuous in the interval* $a \leqslant x \leqslant b$, *then*

$$\int_a^x f(t)g(t)dt = \Big[F(t)g(t)\Big]_a^x - \int_a^x F(t)g'(t)dt,$$

where $a \leqslant x \leqslant b$.

By the rule for the differentiation of a product

$$\frac{d}{dt}\Big[F(t)g(t)\Big] = g(t)\frac{d}{dt}F(t) + F(t)\frac{d}{dt}g(t),$$

which is a continuous function of t in the interval $a \leqslant t \leqslant b$. Using § 31, (10), we have therefore

$$\Big[F(t)g(t)\Big]_a^x = \int_a^x f(t)g(t)dt + \int_a^x F(t)g'(t)dt,$$

where $a \leqslant x \leqslant b$.

§ 45. Theorems of Mean Value

(1) *If* g(x) *is continuous and* f(x) *positive and integrable in the interval* $a \leqslant x \leqslant b$, *then*

$$\int_a^b f(x)g(x)dx = g(\xi) \int_a^b f(x)dx,$$

where $a \leqslant \xi \leqslant b$.

This is known as the *First Integral Theorem of Mean Value.*

By the lemma of § 43, $f(x)g(x)$ is integrable over (a, b). If M, m are the bounds of $g(x)$ in (a, b),

$$mf(x) \leqslant f(x)g(x) \leqslant Mf(x),\ a \leqslant x \leqslant b,$$

and we have at once

$$m \int_a^b f(x)dx \leqslant \int_a^b f(x)g(x)dx \leqslant M \int_a^b f(x)dx,$$

giving, since $g(x)$ is continuous,

$$\int_a^b f(x)g(x)dx \Bigg/ \int_a^b f(x)dx = g(\xi),\ a \leqslant \xi \leqslant b.$$

If $f(x)$ is negative the result still holds, for

$$\int_a^b [-f(x)]g(x)dx = g(\xi) \int_a^b [-f(x)]dx.$$

(2) *If* f(x) *is a positive and* g(x) *a positive decreasing function, both integrable in the interval* $a \leqslant x \leqslant b$, *then*

$$\int_a^b f(x)g(x)dx = g(a) \int_a^\xi f(x)dx,$$

where $a \leqslant \xi \leqslant b$.

Since $f(x)g(x)$ is integrable and $f(x)g(x) \leqslant f(x)g(a)$,

$$\int_a^b f(x)g(x)dx \leqslant g(a) \int_a^b f(x)dx.$$

Now $\int_a^x f(t)dt$ is an increasing continuous function.

Hence

$$\int_a^b f(x)g(x)dx = g(a) \int_a^\xi f(x)dx, \; a \leqslant \xi \leqslant b.$$

If $g(x)$ is a positive increasing function similar reasoning shows that

$$\int_a^b f(x)g(x)dx = g(b) \int_\xi^b f(x)dx, \; a \leqslant \xi \leqslant b.$$

(3) *If* f(x) *is continuous and* g(x) *either increasing or decreasing with* g′(x) *continuous in the interval* $\mathrm{a} \leqslant \mathrm{x} \leqslant \mathrm{b}$, *then*

$$\int_a^b f(x)g(x)dx = g(a) \int_a^\xi f(x)dx + g(b) \int_\xi^b f(x)dx,$$

where $\mathrm{a} \leqslant \xi \leqslant \mathrm{b}$.

This is known as the *Second Integral Theorem of Mean Value.*

If $F(x)$ is an indefinite integral of $f(x)$,

$$\int_a^b f(x)g(x)dx = \Big[F(x)g(x)\Big]_a^b - \int_a^b F(x)g'(x)dx.$$

Now $g'(x)$ does not change sign in (a, b) and we can apply the First Integral Theorem of Mean Value, obtaining

$$\int_a^b f(x)g(x)dx = \Big[F(x)g(x)\Big]_a^b - F(\xi) \int_a^b g'(x)dx, \; a \leqslant \xi \leqslant b,$$

$$= F(b)g(b) - F(a)g(a) - F(\xi)g(b) + F(\xi)g(a)$$

$$= g(a) \int_a^\xi f(x)dx + g(b) \int_\xi^b f(x)dx.$$

§ 46. Integration of Series

The series of functions $u_1(x) + u_2(x) + \ldots$ is said to **converge uniformly** to the function $s(x)$ in the interval $a \leqslant x \leqslant b$, if, given any ϵ, we can find n_0 independent of x such that

$$|u_1(x) + u_2(x) + \ldots + u_n(x) - s(x)| < \epsilon,$$

if $n > n_0$, for every value of x in (a, b). If, further, the functions $u_n(x)$ are continuous in the interval $a \leqslant x \leqslant b$, it can be shown that $s(x)$ is continuous in the interval.

We now prove the following theorem.*

If the series of continuous functions $u_1(x)+u_2(x)+\ldots$ *converges uniformly to* $s(x)$ *in the interval* $a \leqslant x \leqslant b$, *then*

$$\int_a^b u_1(x)dx + \int_a^b u_2(x)dx + \ldots = \int_a^b s(x)dx.$$

Since $s(x)$ is continuous it is integrable over (a, b). If $n > n_0$

$$\left|\int_a^b u_1(x)dx + \int_a^b u_2(x)dx + \ldots + \int_a^b u_n(x)dx - \int_a^b s(x)dx\right|$$
$$\leqslant \int_a^b |u_1(x)+u_2(x)+\ldots+u_n(x)-s(x)|dx$$
$$< \epsilon(b-a).$$

This proves the theorem.

We are enabled by the theorem to expand very easily some functions in power series. From the series

$$1/(1+x^2) = 1-x^2+x^4-\ldots, \ -1<x<1,$$

by integration from 0 to x, we obtain

$$\tan^{-1}x = x - x^3/3 + x^5/5 - x^7/7 + \ldots, \ -1<x<1.$$

We can also evaluate certain integrals by this method. It may happen that we cannot integrate $s(x)$ directly but that we can integrate $u_r(x)$.

For example, $\int_0^1 \frac{1}{x}\log(1+x)dx$ does not easily reduce to a standard form. This integral exists since the integrand is continuous in the interval $0<x\leqslant 1$ and tends to 1 as x tends to zero. Now

$$\int_0^1 \frac{1}{x}\log(1+x)dx = \int_0^1\left(1-\frac{x}{2}+\frac{x^2}{3}-\frac{x^3}{4}+\ldots\right)dx$$
$$= \frac{1}{1^2} - \frac{1}{2^2} + \frac{1}{3^2} - \frac{1}{4^2} + \ldots,$$

a convergent series whose sum is $\pi^2/12$.

* See Hyslop, *Infinite Series*, § 45.

§ 47. Orthogonal Systems of Functions

The set of functions $u_0(x)$, $u_1(x)$, $u_2(x)$, ..., defined in the interval $a \leqslant x \leqslant b$, is said to be **orthogonal** in this interval if

$$\int_a^b u_m(x)u_n(x)dx = 0, \text{ if } m \neq n,$$
$$= k_n > 0, \text{ if } m = n,$$

where $m, n = 0, 1, 2, \ldots$. If, further, $k_n = 1, n = 0, 1, 2, \ldots$, the system is said to be **normal**. It is clear that if the system $\{u_n(x)\}$ is orthogonal, the system $\left\{\frac{u_n(x)}{\sqrt{k_n}}\right\}$ is orthogonal and normal. If the orthogonal system $\{u_n(x)\}$ possesses the property that there exists no integrable function $\phi(x)$, not identically zero, such that

$$\int_a^b \phi(x)u_n(x)dx = 0, \ n = 0, 1, 2, \ldots,$$

and $\phi(x) \not\equiv u_m(x)$, $m = 0, 1, 2, \ldots$, then the system $\{u_n(x)\}$ is said to be **complete**. In other words the system $\{u_n(x)\}$ is complete if no new members can be added to it.

Let the series

$$c_0u_0(x) + c_1u_1(x) + \ldots$$

where c_0, c_1, ... are constants and $\{u_n(x)\}$ is an orthogonal set of continuous functions, converge uniformly in the interval (a, b) to the function $f(x)$. Then, multiplying by $u_n(x)$ and integrating, we obtain by the theorem of § 46

$$c_n = \frac{1}{k_n} \int_a^b f(x)u_n(x)dx.$$

The series

$$\sum_{n=0}^{\infty} \left[\frac{1}{k_n} \int_a^b f(x)u_n(x)dx\right] u_n(x)$$

is called the *Fourier series* of $f(x)$.

We now prove the following theorem :

If f(x) *is continuous and the system* $\{u_n(x)\}$ *is orthogonal and complete in the interval* (a, b), *and if the series*

$$\sum_{n=0}^{\infty}\left[\frac{1}{k_n}\int_a^b f(x)u_n(x)dx\right]u_n(x)$$

is uniformly convergent in (a, b), *then this series converges to* f(x).

Let the series converge to the function $g(x)$. Then

$$\int_a^b f(x)u_n(x)dx = \int_a^b g(x)u_n(x)dx,\ n = 0, 1, \ldots,$$

so that

$$\int_a^b [f(x)-g(x)]u_n(x)dx = 0,\ n = 0, 1, \ldots.$$

Since the system is complete, $f(x)=g(x)$.

As an example of an orthogonal system let us take the set of functions

$$1, \sin x, \cos x, \sin 2x, \cos 2x, \ldots,$$

which, by the results obtained in § 11, (1), (2), is clearly orthogonal in the interval $(-\pi, \pi)$. We now show that this trigonometrical system is complete, *i.e.* we show that no integrable function $f(x)$ exists such that

$$\int_{-\pi}^{\pi} f(x) \sin mx\, dx = 0, \qquad \int_{-\pi}^{\pi} f(x) \cos mx\, dx = 0,$$

where $m = 0, 1, 2, \ldots$. Suppose first that a continuous function $f(x)$, not identically zero in $(-\pi, \pi)$, exists with these properties. Since $f(x) \not\equiv 0$, we can find a point x_0 in the interval where $f(x_0)>0$ [or $f(x_0)<0$]. Given any ϵ, we can find η such that

$$f(x)>\epsilon \text{ where } x_0-\eta\leqslant x\leqslant x_0+\eta.$$

We now take the function

$$\phi_n(x) = [1+\cos(x-x_0)-\cos\eta]^n,$$

where n is a positive integer, which can be expressed as

$$\sum_{m=0}^{n} a_m \cos mx + b_m \sin mx.$$

Thus $\int_{-\pi}^{\pi} f(x)\phi_n(x)dx = 0$. However as $n\to\infty$, $\phi_n(x)$ tends uniformly to $+\infty$ in every interval inside $(x_0-\eta,\ x_0+\eta)$ and $\phi_n(x)$ is uniformly bounded outside this interval. This contradicts the statement

$$\int_{-\pi}^{\pi} f(x)\phi_n(x)dx = 0.$$

Assuming now that $f(x)$ is merely integrable, let

$$F(x) = \int_{-\pi}^{x} f(t)dt,$$

so that $F(x)$ is continuous in the interval $(-\pi, \pi)$, [§ 31, (7)]. By integration by parts,*

$$\int_{-\pi}^{\pi} F(x)\sin mx\, dx = 0,$$

$$\int_{-\pi}^{\pi} F(x)\cos mx\, dx = 0, m = 1, 2, \ldots;$$

* We require here a slightly more general form of the theorem than that proved in § 44. This latter part of the proof is rather advanced. The final statement $f(x)\equiv 0$ means that $f(x)$ is everywhere zero except for a set of measure zero. See Hobson, *Functions of a Real Variable*, Vol. I, p. 451.

hence the continuous function

$$F(x)-\frac{1}{2\pi}\int_{-\pi}^{\pi}F(x)dx,$$

by the first part of the proof, is identically zero in $(-\pi, \pi)$. Thus $F(x)$ is constant in the interval, and since $F(-\pi)=0$, $F(x)$ is zero in $(-\pi, \pi)$. It follows that $f(x)\equiv 0$ in the interval.

Another important system of orthogonal functions is that of **Legendre polynomials.** Let *

$$P_n(x)=\frac{1}{2^n \,.\, n\,!}\frac{d^n}{dx^n}(x^2-1)^n\,;$$

then $P_n(x)$ is a polynomial of degree n in x, the Legendre polynomial of degree n. We now show that these polynomials form an orthogonal system in the interval $(-1, 1)$.

Let m and n be positive integers, where $m>n$; then

$$\int_{-1}^{1}P_m(x)P_n(x)dx=$$

$$\frac{1}{2^{m+n}m!\,n!}\int_{-1}^{1}\frac{d^m}{dx^m}(x^2-1)^m\frac{d^n}{dx^n}(x^2-1)^n\,dx,$$

giving, on integration by parts,

$$\frac{1}{2^{m+n}\,m!\,n!}\left[\frac{d^{m-1}}{dx^{m-1}}(x^2-1)^m\frac{d^n}{dx^n}(x^2-1)^n\right]_{-1}^{1}$$

$$-\frac{1}{2^{m+n}\,m!\,n!}\int_{-1}^{1}\frac{d^{m-1}}{dx^{m-1}}(x^2-1)^m\frac{d^{n+1}}{dx^{n+1}}(x^2-1)^n\,dx.$$

* Ince, *Integration of Ordinary Differential Equations*, p. 122.

Clearly the first term of this expression is zero. We integrate by parts in this way n times altogether and obtain

$$\int_{-1}^{1} P_m(x)P_n(x)dx$$

$$= \frac{(-1)^n}{2^{m+n}\, m!\, n!} \int_{-1}^{1} \frac{d^{m-n}}{dx^{m-n}} (x^2-1)^m \frac{d^{2n}}{dx^{2n}} (x^2-1)^n dx$$

$$= \frac{(-1)^n\,(2n)!}{2^{m+n}\, m!\, n!} \left[\frac{d^{m-n-1}}{dx^{m-n-1}} (x^2-1)^m\right]_{-1}^{1}$$

$$= 0.$$

Again, using the above process we find that

$$\int_{-1}^{1} [P_n(x)]^2 dx = \frac{(-1)^n(2n)!}{2^{2n}(n!)^2} \int_{-1}^{1} \frac{d^{n-n}}{dx^{n-n}} (x^2-1)^n dx$$

$$= \frac{(2n)!}{2^{2n}(n!)^2} \int_{-1}^{1} (1-x^2)^n dx$$

$$= \frac{2(2n)!}{2^{2n}(n!)^2} \int_{0}^{\frac{\pi}{2}} \cos^{2n+1}\theta\, d\theta$$

$$= \frac{2}{2n+1}.$$

§ 48. Differentiation under the Integral Sign

Let $f(x,y)$ be a function which is continuous with respect to the pair of variables (x, y) in the closed rectangle $a \leqslant x \leqslant b$, $\alpha \leqslant y \leqslant \beta$, and let $\phi_1(x)$, $\phi_2(x)$ be continuous functions of x such that $\alpha \leqslant \phi_1(x) \leqslant \phi_2(x) \leqslant \beta$ in the interval $a \leqslant x \leqslant b$. We shall integrate $f(x,y)$ with respect to y, keeping x constant, from $y = \phi_1(x)$ to $y = \phi_2(x)$. With x constant and lying in (a, b), it can be easily seen that $f(x, y)$ is a continuous function of y when y is in the interval $\phi_1(x) \leqslant y \leqslant \phi_2(x)$. Hence the integral

$$\int_{\phi_1(x)}^{\phi_2(x)} f(x, y)dy$$

exists, and, since its value depends on the particular x chosen, it is a function of x, $\phi(x)$ say. We are now going to show that $\phi(x)$ is continuous in the interval (a, b). We have

$$|\phi(x+h)-\phi(x)| = \left| \int_{\phi_1(x+h)}^{\phi_2(x+h)} f(x+h, y)dy - \int_{\phi_1(x)}^{\phi_2(x)} f(x, y)dy \right|$$

$$= \left| \int_{\phi_1(x)}^{\phi_2(x)} \{f(x+h, y)-f(x, y)\}dy + \int_{\phi_2(x)}^{\phi_2(x+h)} f(x+h, y)dy - \int_{\phi_1(x)}^{\phi_1(x+h)} f(x+h, y)dy \right|$$

$$\leqslant \int_{\phi_1(x)}^{\phi_2(x)} |f(x+h, y)-f(x, y)|dy + \left| \int_{\phi_2(x)}^{\phi_2(x+h)} |f(x+h, y)|dy \right| + \left| \int_{\phi_1(x)}^{\phi_1(x+h)} |f(x+h, y)|dy \right|.$$

Given any ϵ, we can choose η_1, η_2, η_3, so that

$$|f(x+h, y)-f(x, y)| < \epsilon, \text{ where } |h| < \eta_1,$$

and η_1 is the same for all values of y in the interval $\alpha \leqslant y \leqslant \beta$;

$$|\phi_1(x+h)-\phi_1(x)| < \epsilon, \text{ where } |h| < \eta_2;$$
$$|\phi_2(x+h)-\phi_2(x)| < \epsilon, \text{ where } |h| < \eta_3.$$

Hence

$$|\phi(x+h)-\phi(x)| < (\beta-\alpha)\epsilon + 2M\epsilon, \text{ where } |h| < \eta,$$

η being the smallest of η_1, η_2 η_3 and M the maximum value of $|f(x, y)|$ in the rectangle. Thus $\phi(x)$ is continuous in the interval $a \leqslant x \leqslant b$.

We now assume further that $\partial f/\partial x$ is continuous with respect to the pair of variables (x, y) in the closed rectangle and that $\phi_1'(x)$, $\phi_2'(x)$ exist in the interval $a \leqslant x \leqslant b$. With these conditions we shall obtain the derivative of $\phi(x)$. Since $\partial f/\partial x$ is continuous, the integral

$$\int_{\phi_1(x)}^{\phi_2(x)} \frac{\partial f}{\partial x}\, dy$$

exists in the interval $a \leqslant x \leqslant b$. Now

$$\frac{\phi(x+h)-\phi(x)}{h} - \int_{\phi_1(x)}^{\phi_2(x)} \frac{\partial f}{\partial x}\, dy = \int_{\phi_1(x)}^{\phi_2(x)} \left\{ \frac{f(x+h, y)-f(x, y)}{h} - \frac{\partial f}{\partial x} \right\} dy$$

$$+ \frac{1}{h} \int_{\phi_2(x)}^{\phi_2(x+h)} f(x+h, y)dy - \frac{1}{h} \int_{\phi_1(x)}^{\phi_1(x+h)} f(x+h, y)dy.$$

But

$$\frac{f(x+h, y)-f(x, y)}{h} = \frac{\partial f(x+\theta_1 h, y)}{\partial x}, \text{ where } 0<\theta_1<1,$$

since $\partial f/\partial x$ exists. Hence the first integral on the right tends to zero as $h \to 0$. Since $f(x+h, y)$ is for fixed x a continuous function of y, we have, by § 31, (8),

$$\frac{1}{h} \int_{\phi_2(x)}^{\phi_2(x+h)} f(x+h, y)dy = \frac{\phi_2(x+h)-\phi_2(x)}{h} f(x+h, \xi)$$

where ξ is some number between $\phi_2(x)$ and $\phi_2(x+h)$. Now $\phi_2(x)$ is continuous so that ξ may be written in the form $\phi_2(x+\theta_2 h)$, $0 \leqslant \theta_2 \leqslant 1$. Hence the second and third integrals are respectively equal to

$$\frac{\phi_2(x+h)-\phi_2(x)}{h} f[x+h, \phi_2(x+\theta_2 h)],$$

and
$$-\frac{\phi_1(x+h)-\phi_1(x)}{h} f[x+h, \phi_1(x+\theta_3 h)],\ 0 \leqslant \theta_3 \leqslant 1.$$

H 2

As $h \to 0$, these integrals tend to $\phi_2'(x)f[x, \phi_2(x)]$ and $-\phi_1'(x)f[x, \phi_1(x)]$. Hence $\phi'(x)$ exists and is equal to

$$\int_{\phi_1(x)}^{\phi_2(x)} \frac{\partial f(x, y)}{\partial x} dy + f[x, \phi_2(x)]\phi_2'(x) - f[x, \phi_1(x)]\phi_1'(x).$$

If $\phi_1(x) \equiv \alpha$, $\phi_2(x) \equiv \beta$, we have

$$\frac{d}{dx} \int_a^\beta f(x, y) dy = \int_a^\beta \frac{\partial f(x, y)}{\partial x} dy.$$

This process is called **differentiation under the integral sign.**

§ 49. Double Integral Over a Rectangle

We begin the discussion of the double integral by defining the integral over a rectangle. The definition over a field bounded by a closed curve raises difficulties which will be discussed later. Let $f(x,y)$ be a function defined and bounded in the region A, $a \leqslant x \leqslant b$, $c \leqslant y \leqslant d$. The rectangle A is divided as in § 13 by lines $x = x_0, x_1, \ldots, x_m$ and $y = y_0, y_1, \ldots, y_n$, where

$$a = x_0 < x_1 < \ldots < x_m = b, \; c = y_0 < y_1 < \ldots < y_n = d.$$

This divides the region into mn rectangles A_{rs}, $x_{r-1} \leqslant x \leqslant x_r$, $y_{s-1} \leqslant y \leqslant y_s$. In each rectangle A_{rs} any point (ξ_{rs}, η_{rs}) is taken and the sum

$$\Sigma = \sum_{\substack{r=1,m \\ s=1,n}} f(\xi_{rs}, \eta_{rs}) \,.\, (x_r - x_{r-1})(y_s - y_{s-1})$$

is formed. The function $f(x, y)$ is said to be **integrable over the region A** if, given any ϵ, there exists a number I and a non-zero number δ such that for every way of dividing A into small rectangles A_{rs} for which $x_r - x_{r-1} < \delta$, $y_s - y_{s-1} < \delta$ and for every way of choosing the point

(ξ_{rs}, η_{rs}) in A_{rs}, $|\Sigma - I| < \epsilon$. The number I is the **double integral** of $f(x, y)$ over A and is written

$$\iint_A f(x, y)dx\,dy.$$

If $f(x, y) \equiv 1$, the integral clearly exists and the double integral is the area of the rectangle A.

We now prove a theorem similar to that of § 29, the method of proof following similar lines. We first define **upper and lower sums** corresponding to any particular method of division into rectangles. If M_{rs}, m_{rs} are the upper and lower bounds of $f(x, y)$ in A_{rs},

$$\mathbf{S} = \sum_{\substack{r=1,m \\ s=1,n}} M_{rs}(x_r - x_{r-1})(y_s - y_{s-1}),$$

$$\mathbf{s} = \sum_{\substack{r=1,m \\ s=1,n}} m_{rs}(x_r - x_{r-1})(y_s - y_{s-1})$$

are the upper and lower sums of $f(x, y)$ corresponding to this particular method of dividing A. Exactly as in § 29 we have

(i) $\mathbf{s} \leqslant \Sigma \leqslant \mathbf{S}$,

(ii) $m(b-a)(d-c) \leqslant \mathbf{s} \leqslant \mathbf{S} \leqslant M(b-a)(d-c)$,

where m, M are the bounds of $f(x, y)$ in A.

(iii) If $\mathbf{s}$, $\mathbf{S}$ are the lower and upper sums corresponding to some method of dividing the rectangle, and if new points of division are added to the x_r or to the y_s or to both, giving new sums $\mathbf{s}_1$, $\mathbf{S}_1$, then

$$\mathbf{s} \leqslant \mathbf{s}_1 \leqslant \mathbf{S}_1 \leqslant \mathbf{S}.$$

This follows as in § 29, and as there we deduce that every lower sum is less than or equal to every upper sum. Hence the upper sums have a lower bound J and the lower sums an upper bound I, and $I \leqslant J$. The following theorem follows exactly as in the case of the single integral.

If, given any ϵ, *we can find* δ *such that, for all methods of dividing* A *into small rectangles by lines* $x = x_r$, $y = y_s$ *in which* $x_r - x_{r-1} < \delta$, $y_s - y_{s-1} < \delta$, $|\mathbf{S} - \mathbf{s}| < \epsilon$, *then* f(x,y) *is integrable over* A *and*

$$\iint_A f(x, y)dxdy = I = J.$$

We shall now show that if $f(x, y)$ is continuous with respect to the pair of variables (x, y) in the closed rectangle A, $f(x, y)$ is integrable over A. The theorem of uniform continuity states that if $f(x, y)$ is continuous with respect to the pair of variables in a closed region A it is uniformly continuous in this region ; *i.e.* given any ϵ, we can find δ, the same for all (x_0, y_0) in A, such that

$$|f(x, y) - f(x_0, y_0)| < \frac{\epsilon}{(b-a)(d-c)}, \text{ if } |x - x_0| < \delta,\ |y - y_0| < \delta,$$

and (x, y) lies in A. We divide the rectangle as above into small rectangles so that the length and breadth of each small rectangle is less than δ. Now the upper and lower bounds of $f(x, y)$ in A_{rs}, M_{rs} and m_{rs}, are values of the function, say $f(\xi_{rs}, \eta_{rs})$ and $f(\xi'_{rs}, \eta'_{rs})$, where (ξ_{rs}, η_{rs}), (ξ'_{rs}, η'_{rs}) lie in A_{rs}. Then

$$\begin{aligned}\mathbf{S} - \mathbf{s} &= \Sigma M_{rs}A_{rs} - \Sigma m_{rs}A_{rs}\\ &= \Sigma[f(\xi_{rs}, \eta_{rs}) - f(\xi'_{rs}, \eta'_{rs})]A_{rs}.\end{aligned}$$

Now $|\xi_{rs} - \xi'_{rs}| < \delta$, $|\eta_{rs} - \eta'_{rs}| < \delta$, and so

$$f(\xi_{rs}, \eta_{rs}) - f(\xi'_{rs}, \eta'_{rs}) < \frac{\epsilon}{(b-a)(d-c)};$$

hence

$$\mathbf{S} - \mathbf{s} < \frac{\epsilon}{(b-a)(d-c)} \Sigma A_{rs} = \epsilon,$$

which proves that $f(x, y)$ is integrable over A.

§ 50. Rectifiable Curves

Before we can define what we mean by an *area* enclosed by a curve we must obtain a definition of what we mean by a *curve*. Let $\phi(t)$, $\psi(t)$ be two single-valued functions of t defined for the interval $\alpha \leqslant t \leqslant \beta$. The set of values (x, y) given by $x = \phi(t)$, $y = \psi(t)$, $\alpha \leqslant t \leqslant \beta$, is said to define a **curve.** If $\phi(t)$, $\psi(t)$ are continuous functions the curve thus defined is called a **continuous curve.** If $\phi(t)$, $\psi(t)$ are periodic functions having the same period, the curve is called a **closed curve** ; *e.g.* the curve $x = \cos t$, $y = \sin t$ is the closed curve, the circle $x^2+y^2 = 1$. If two or more values of t give identical values of x and y, these values are said to define a **multiple point** on the curve. A curve without multiple points is called a **simple curve.** We shall assume that a simple closed continuous curve divides the plane into two parts, a part inside and a part outside the curve.

We now give a definition of the **length** of a curve and find conditions which $\phi(t)$, $\psi(t)$ must satisfy in order that the curve $x = \phi(t)$, $y = \psi(t)$ may possess length, or as we say, be **rectifiable.** Let C be a continuous curve defined by the equations $x = \phi(t)$, $y = \psi(t)$, where $\phi(t)$, $\psi(t)$ are single-valued continuous functions in the interval $\alpha \leqslant t \leqslant \beta$. This interval is now divided into any finite number of parts, not necessarily equal, by points $t_0, t_1, \ldots, t_n$, where $\alpha = t_0 < t_1 < \ldots < t_n = \beta$, and the sum

$$\Sigma = \sum_{r=1}^{n} \sqrt{[\{\phi(t_r)-\phi(t_{r-1})\}^2+\{\psi(t_r)-\psi(t_{r-1})\}^2]}$$

is formed. In geometrical language this is the length of the polygonal line formed by joining in turn the points of the curve C given by the values $t_0, t_1, \ldots, t_n$ of the parameter t. Let L denote the upper bound of the set of all possible values of Σ. This upper bound is either a positive finite number or is $+\infty$. If it is finite it is called the *length* of the curve C, and the curve is rectifiable.

We now prove the following theorem:

If the upper bound L of the set of all possible values of Σ is finite, then, given any ϵ, we can find η such that

$$L-\epsilon<\Sigma\leqslant L,$$

provided only that $t_r-t_{r-1}<\eta$ *for all* r *concerned.*

We require the inequality

$$\begin{aligned}&\sqrt{[\{\phi(b)-\phi(a)\}^2+\{\psi(b)-\psi(a)\}^2]}\\&+\sqrt{[\{\phi(c)-\phi(b)\}^2+\{\psi(c)-\psi(b)\}^2]}\\&\geqslant\sqrt{[\{\phi(c)-\phi(a)\}^2+\{\psi(c)-\psi(a)\}^2]},\end{aligned}$$

which may be proved by squaring twice.

Let (t_r), $r = 0, 1, \ldots, n$, be a set of points of division of (α, β) for which $\Sigma = \Sigma_1>L-\frac{1}{2}\epsilon$. Corresponding to any positive number σ, we can find, since ϕ and ψ are continuous functions, a non-zero number η such that

$$\sqrt{[\{\phi(\lambda)-\phi(\mu)\}^2+\{\psi(\lambda)-\psi(\mu)\}^2]}<\sigma,$$

if $|\lambda-\mu|<\eta$ and λ, μ belong to (α, β). Let (τ_s), $s = 0, 1, \ldots, m$, be a second set of points of division of (α, β) for which $\tau_s-\tau_{s-1}<\eta$ and let Σ_2 denote the value of Σ for this second method of division. Let Σ_3 denote the value of Σ obtained by taking the points (t_r) and (τ_s) together as points of division. It follows from the above inequality that $\Sigma_3>L-\frac{1}{2}\epsilon$. The intervals of the (τ_s) division which do not contain in their interior points t_r make the same contribution Σ_4 to Σ_2 as they do to Σ_3, and clearly $\Sigma_2\geqslant\Sigma_4$. Let us now consider the remainder of the (τ_s) divisions, of which there cannot be more than $n-1$. They make a contribution to Σ_3 which is less than $2(n-1)\sigma$; (the case when one t_r occurs in each of the remainder divisions is the most unfavourable and the contribution in this case is less than $2(n-1)\sigma$). It follows that

$$\Sigma_3<\Sigma_4+2(n-1)\sigma,$$

and so

$$\Sigma_2\geqslant\Sigma_4>\Sigma_3-2(n-1)\sigma>L-\tfrac{1}{2}\epsilon-2(n-1)\sigma.$$

Now n depends only on ϵ, and if we choose $\sigma<\epsilon/4(n-1)$, we have $\Sigma_2>L-\epsilon$. This proves the theorem.

It is clear that if the curve is rectifiable the sums

$$\sum_{r=1}^{n}|\phi(t_r)-\phi(t_{r-1})| \quad , \quad \sum_{r=1}^{n}|\psi(t_r)-\psi(t_{r-1})|$$

must be bounded for all ways of dividing the interval (α, β) by points t_r. If the functions $\phi(t)$, $\psi(t)$ satisfy this condition they are said to be **functions of bounded variation** over the interval (α,β). Thus a necessary condition that the curve be rectifiable is that $\phi(t)$, $\psi(t)$ are of bounded variation in (α, β). It is easy to see that the condition is also sufficient, for, since

$$\sqrt{[\{\phi(b)-\phi(a)\}^2+\{\psi(b)-\psi(a)\}^2]} \leqslant|\phi(b)-\phi(a)|+|\psi(b)-\psi(a)|,$$

it is clear that when ϕ and ψ are of bounded variation the upper bound of Σ is finite and the curve is rectifiable.

§ 51. Theorem

If $\phi'(t)$, $\psi'(t)$ *exist for the interval* $\alpha\leqslant t\leqslant\beta$, *the curve* $x=\phi(t)$, $y=\psi(t)$ *is rectifiable. If, further,* $\phi'(t)$, $\psi'(t)$ *are integrable over* (α, β), *the length of the curve is given by*

$$\int_{\alpha}^{\beta}\sqrt{[\{\phi'(t)\}^2+\{\psi'(t)\}^2]}dt.$$

Since $\phi'(t)$, $\psi'(t)$ exist in the interval $\alpha\leqslant t\leqslant\beta$, the functions $\phi(t)$, $\psi(t)$ are continuous in (α, β). Again, since $\phi'(t)$ exists we can apply the mean value theorem and obtain

$$\phi(t_r)-\phi(t_{r-1}) = (t_r-t_{r-1})\phi'(\tau_r), \text{ where } t_{r-1}<\tau_r<t_r.$$

Hence $$|\phi(t_r)-\phi(t_{r-1})| = (t_r-t_{r-1})|\phi'(\tau_r)|,$$

and so $$\Sigma|\phi(t_r)-\phi(t_{r-1})|\leqslant(\beta-\alpha)M,$$

where M is the upper bound of $|\phi'(t)|$ in (α, β). Thus

$\phi(t)$, $\psi(t)$ are of bounded variation in (α, β) and, by the previous paragraph, the curve $x = \phi(t)$, $y = \psi(t)$ is rectifiable.

If we are given further that $\phi'(t)$, $\psi'(t)$ are integrable we can show that $\sqrt{[\{\phi'(t)\}^2 + \{\psi'(t)\}^2]}$ is integrable. Let M_r, m_r ; M_r^1, m_r^1 ; $\bar{M}_r$, $\bar{m}_r$ be the bounds of $\phi'(t)$, $\psi'(t)$, $\sqrt{[\phi'^2 + \psi'^2]}$ respectively in the interval (t_{r-1}, t_r). Then

$$\bar{M}_r - \bar{m}_r \leqslant \sqrt{(M_r^2 + M_r^{12})} - \sqrt{(m_r^2 + m_r^{12})}$$

$$\leqslant (M_r - m_r) + (M_r^1 - m_r^1),$$

since

$$\sqrt{(M_r^2 + M_r^{12})} - \sqrt{(m_r^2 + m_r^{12})}$$

$$= \frac{(M_r - m_r)(M_r + m_r) + (M_r^1 - m_r^1)(M_r^1 + m_r^1)}{\sqrt{(M_r^2 + M_r^{12})} + \sqrt{(m_r^2 + m_r^{12})}}.$$

It follows at once that $\sqrt{[\phi'^2 + \psi'^2]}$ is integrable.

The length of the curve is the number L with the property that, given any ϵ, we can find η such that

$$L - \epsilon < \Sigma \leqslant L,$$

where $\Sigma = \Sigma \sqrt{[\{\phi(t_r) - \phi(t_{r-1})\}^2 + \{\psi(t_r) - \psi(t_{r-1})\}^2]}$, provided only that $t_r - t_{r-1} < \eta$. Now

$$\phi(t_r) - \phi(t_{r-1}) = \phi'(\tau_r) \,.\, (t_r - t_{r-1}), \text{ where } t_{r-1} < \tau_r < t_r,$$

and $\psi(t_r) - \psi(t_{r-1}) = \psi'(\tau_r') \,.\, (t_r - t_{r-1})$, where $t_{r-1} < \tau_r' < t_r$;

hence $\quad \Sigma = \Sigma (t_r - t_{r-1}) \sqrt{[\{\phi'(\tau_r)\}^2 + \{\psi'(\tau_r')\}^2]}$.

Again, the integral of $\sqrt{[\phi'^2 + \psi'^2]}$ over (α, β) is a number L' with the following property: given any ϵ, we can find η such that $|L' - \Sigma'| < \epsilon$, provided only $t_r - t_{r-1} < \eta$, where

$$\Sigma' = \Sigma (t_r - t_{r-1}) \sqrt{[\{\phi'(\lambda_r)\}^2 + \{\psi'(\lambda_r)\}^2]},$$

and λ_r is any point of the interval (t_{r-1}, t_r). As above

$$|\sqrt{[\{\phi'(\tau_r)\}^2+\{\psi'(\tau_r')\}^2]}-\sqrt{[\{\phi'(\lambda_r)\}^2+\{\psi'(\lambda_r)\}^2]}|$$
$$\leqslant|\phi'(\tau_r)-\phi'(\lambda_r)|+|\psi'(\tau_r')-\psi'(\lambda_r)|$$
$$\leqslant(M_r-m_r)+(M_r^1-m_r^1),$$

and, since ϕ', ψ' are integrable, $L' = L$.

§ 52. Double Integrals

We now define the double integral over a field enclosed by a simple rectifiable curve. As in § 13 (page 30) let ABC be a simple closed rectifiable curve lying entirely inside the rectangle $x = a$, $x = b$, $y = c$, $y = d$. Let $f(x,y)$ be continuous with respect to the pair of variables (x,y) inside and on ABC. We define $F(x,y)$ as equal to $f(x,y)$ inside and on ABC and as zero outside the curve, and show that $F(x, y)$ is integrable over the rectangle.

In general $F(x,y)$ is not continuous in the rectangle, but it is clear that its discontinuities are limited to points on the curve ABC. As in § 49 the rectangle is divided by lines $x = x_r$, $y = y_s$ into mn small rectangles and the sum

$$\Sigma\, F(\xi_{rs}, \eta_{rs}) \cdot (x_r-x_{r-1})(y_s-y_{s-1})$$

is formed. The small rectangles can be divided into two classes : A_1, those which contain points of the curve ABC, and A_2, those which do not.

If L denotes the length of the curve, and (x_1, y_1), (x_2, y_2) are any two points on the curve, it is clear from the inequality in § 50 that

$$L\geqslant\sqrt{\{(x_1-x_2)^2+(y_1-y_2)^2\}}.$$

We divide the curve into p parts each of length L/p and set up squares with the points of division of the curve as centres and with sides parallel to the axes and of length

$4L/p$. By choosing max. $(x_r - x_{r-1})$, max. $(y_s - y_{s-1})$ small enough we can ensure that the set of rectangles A_1 lies entirely inside the set of squares. The total area of the squares is $16L^2(p+1)/p^2$, and this can be made as small as we please by taking p large enough. Thus, given any ϵ, we can make the contribution to $\mathbf{S}-\mathbf{s}$ from the rectangles A_1 less than $(M-m)\epsilon$, where M, m are the bounds of $F(x,y)$ in the whole rectangle. In the rectangles A_2, $F(x,y)$ is continuous and we can make the contribution to $\mathbf{S}-\mathbf{s}$ as small as we please by taking max. $(x_r - x_{r-1})$, max. $(y_s - y_{s-1})$ small enough. Hence $F(x,y)$ is integrable over the rectangle. This integral is the double integral of $f(x,y)$ over the field enclosed by the curve ABC.

We are now in a position to define the **area** of the figure enclosed by a rectifiable curve.

The measure of the **area** of the figure enclosed by the rectifiable curve ABC is defined to be the value of the integral.

$$\iint_{ABC} dx\, dy$$

This integral of course exists since $f(x, y) \equiv 1$ is continuous.

§ 53. Repeated Integrals

In this paragraph we give a rigorous treatment of the transformation of a double integral into a repeated integral which was discussed in § 14. Let the double integral be that of $f(x,y)$ over the area enclosed by the rectifiable curve ABC. As in § 14 (Fig. 5, page 34), let the curve be enclosed by the smallest possible rectangle with sides $(x = a,\ x = b;\ y = c,\ y = d)$ parallel to the axes. We assume that any line parallel to the axes meets the curve in at most two points. By the last paragraph we know that the double integral exists. If we have a rule giving for each pair of integers (m, n) a particular way of dividing (a, b) into m parts and (c, d) into n parts and a particular way of choosing $(\xi_{rs}^{mn}, \eta_{rs}^{mn})$ in the small rectangle $(x_r^m - x_{r-1}^m, y_s^n - y_{s-1}^n)$, then the sum

$$\Sigma_{mn} = \sum_{\substack{r=1,m\\ s=1,n}} F(\xi_{rs}^{mn}, \eta_{rs}^{mn}) \,.\, (x_r^m - x_{r-1}^m)(y_s^n - y_{s-1}^n)$$

depends only on m and n. Given any ϵ, we can find η, such that

$$|I - \Sigma_{mn}| < \epsilon, \text{ if } \max. (x_r^m - x_{r-1}^m) < \eta, \quad \max. (y_s^n - y_{s-1}^n) < \eta,$$

where I is the double integral of $f(x, y)$ over the figure ABC. Thus

$$I = \lim_{\substack{m\to\infty\\ n\to\infty}} \Sigma_{mn},$$

it being understood that as $m, n \to \infty$ each $x_r^m - x_{r-1}^m$, $y_s^n - y_{s-1}^n$ tends to zero. We now adopt the following simple rule :

(i) we divide (a, b), (c, d) into m, n equal parts,

(ii) in the small rectangle $(x_r - x_{r-1}, y_s - y_{s-1})$ we choose as $(\xi_{rs}^{mn}, \eta_{rs}^{mn})$ the point (x_r, y_s). With this rule

$$\Sigma_{mn} = \sum_{\substack{r=1,m\\ s=1,n}} F(x_r, y_s) \frac{b-a}{m} \frac{d-c}{n}.$$

We now show that the repeated limits

$$\lim_{m\to\infty} \lim_{n\to\infty} \Sigma_{mn}, \quad \lim_{n\to\infty} \lim_{m\to\infty} \Sigma_{mn}$$

exist, and then use the theorem which states that if the double and the two repeated limits exist, they must all three be equal in value. Now

$$\lim_{m\to\infty} \lim_{n\to\infty} \Sigma_{mn} = \lim_{m\to\infty} \sum_{r=1}^{m} \frac{b-a}{m} \left[\lim_{n\to\infty} \sum_{s=1}^{n} F(x_r, y_s) \frac{d-c}{n} \right],$$

but since $F(x_r, y)$ is a continuous function of y in (c, d) except for two possible discontinuities at $y = \phi_1(x_r)$,

$y = \phi_2(x_r)$ (see § 14 for notation), the integral of $F(x_r, y)$ from $y = c$ to $y = d$ exists and is equal to

$$\lim_{n\to\infty} \sum_{s=1}^{n} F(x_r,\ y_s)\ \frac{d-c}{n}.$$

This integral is
$$\int_{\phi_1(x_r)}^{\phi_2(x_r)} f(x_r,\ y)dy,$$

and, since $\phi_1(x)$, $\phi_2(x)$ are continuous, the integral is a continuous function of x_r, $\phi(x_r)$, (by § 48). Now $\phi(x)$ is continuous in (a, b), so $\int_a^b \phi(x)dx$ exists and is equal to

$$\lim_{m\to\infty} \sum_{r=1}^{m} \frac{b-a}{m}\ \phi(x_r).$$

Hence

$$\lim_{m\to\infty} \lim_{n\to\infty} \Sigma_{mn} = \int_a^b \left[\int_{\phi_1(x)}^{\phi_2(x)} f(x,\ y)dy \right] dx,$$

and similarly

$$\lim_{n\to\infty} \lim_{m\to\infty} \Sigma_{mn} = \int_c^d \left[\int_{\psi_1(y)}^{\psi_2(y)} f(x,\ y)dx \right] dy.$$

Finally we have

$$\iint_{ABC} f(x, y)dx\, dy = \int_a^b dx \int_{\phi_1(x)}^{\phi_2(x)} f(x,y)dy = \int_c^d dy \int_{\psi_1(y)}^{\psi_2(y)} f(x,y)dx.$$

Let us now consider the area $ABDC$ (Fig. 2, page 3), where CD is an arc of the rectifiable curve with equation $y = f(x)$. The area $ABDC$ is given by

$$\iint_{ABDC} dx\, dy,$$

which can be expressed as the repeated integral

$$\int_a^b dx \int_0^{f(x)} dy = \int_a^b f(x)dx.$$

§ 54. The Generalised Element of Area

Let A denote a part of the (x,y) plane bounded by rectifiable curves, and $f(x, y)$ a function continuous with respect to the pair of variables inside and on the boundary of this field. Suppose the field is divided into small portions by a set of rectifiable curves and let ΔS be a representative portion. Then ΔS, being bounded by rectifiable curves, has a definite area, which we denote by the same symbol ΔS. If (x, y) is any point belonging to the closed area ΔS and if the sum

$$\Sigma = \Sigma f(x, y)\Delta S$$

is formed over all the small areas in A, we shall show that there exists a definite number I such that, given any ϵ, we can find η, such that $|I-\Sigma|<\epsilon$, provided only that each ΔS can be enclosed in a square of side less than η.

We define upper and lower sums corresponding to any particular division of A by rectifiable curves, and the whole procedure of § 49 holds. We have, as there, the theorem that if, given any ϵ, we can find η, such that $\mathbf{S}-\mathbf{s}<\epsilon$ provided only that each small portion can be enclosed in a square of side less than η, then the number I exists. Since $f(x, y)$ is continuous with respect to the pair of variables (x, y) inside and on the boundary of A, given any ϵ, we can find η, the same for all (x_0, y_0) in A such that

$$|f(x, y)-f(x_0, y_0)|<\epsilon/A,$$

where A denotes the area of A, if (x, y) lies in A and $|x-x_0|<\sqrt{2}\eta$, $|y-y_0|<\sqrt{2}\eta$. We divide the area A into small areas ΔS by rectifiable curves so that each ΔS lies inside a square of side of length η. Now the bounds of $f(x,y)$ in ΔS are values $f(\xi',\eta')$, $f(\xi'',\eta'')$ of the function, where (ξ', η'), (ξ'', η'') lie in ΔS. Hence

$$\mathbf{S}-\mathbf{s} = \Sigma|f(\xi', \eta')-f(\xi'', \eta'')|\Delta S,$$

and since $|\xi'-\xi''|<\sqrt{2}\eta,\ |\eta'-\eta''|<\sqrt{2}\eta,$

$$\mathbf{S}-\mathbf{s}<\frac{\epsilon}{A}\,\Sigma\Delta S=\epsilon.$$

Thus the number I exists. It is written

$$\iint_A f(x, y)dS.$$

Since division by straight lines parallel to the axes is a special case of this division,

$$\iint_A f(x, y)dS = \iint_A f(x, y)dx\,dy.$$

Examples V

1. Show that if $f(x)$ is bounded and monotone in the interval $a \leqslant x \leqslant b$, it is integrable in this interval.

2. The function $f(x)$ is defined as follows:

(i) $f(x) = 0$, when x is any irrational real number in the interval $(0, 1)$,

(ii) $f(x) = 1/q$, when $x = p/q$, where p/q is any rational real number in the interval $(0, 1)$ in its simplest form.

Show that $f(x)$ is integrable over $(0, 1)$.

3. If $f(x)$ is integrable and $0<k\leqslant f(x)\leqslant K$ in the interval $a\leqslant x\leqslant b$, prove that the function $1/f(x)$ is also integrable in this interval.

4. If $f(x)$, $\phi(x)$ are continuous functions in the interval $a\leqslant x\leqslant b$ and if

$$\int_a^p f(x)dx = \int_a^p \phi(x)dx,$$

where p is any rational real number in the interval (a, b), show that $f(x)\equiv\phi(x)$ in this interval.

5. Prove that

$$\lim_{n\to\infty} n\left[\frac{1}{n^2+1^2}+\frac{1}{n^2+2^2}+\ldots+\frac{1}{2n^2}\right]=\frac{\pi}{4}.$$

6. If $f(x)$ is positive and monotone decreasing for $x \geqslant 1$, and if, for all positive integral values of n,

$$u_n = f(1)+f(2)+f(3)+\ldots+f(n)-\int_1^n f(x)dx,$$

prove that the sequence (u_n) converges to a limit between 0 and $f(1)$.

7. Show that

(i) $$\int_0^1 \log x \log(1+x)dx = 2-2\log 2-\frac{1}{12}\pi^2,$$

(ii) $$\int_0^\theta \log(1+\tan\theta\tan x)dx = \theta\log\sec\theta,$$

where $$-\frac{\pi}{2}<\theta<\frac{\pi}{2}.$$

8. Show that, if $|x|\leqslant 1$,

$$\int_0^1 \frac{1-t}{1-xt^3}\,dt = \frac{1}{1.2}+\frac{x}{4.5}+\frac{x^2}{7.8}+\ldots,$$

and deduce that

(i) $$\frac{1}{1.2}+\frac{1}{4.5}+\frac{1}{7.8}+\ldots=\frac{\pi}{3\sqrt{3}},$$

(ii) $$\frac{1}{1.2}+\frac{1}{7.8}+\frac{1}{13.14}+\ldots=\frac{\pi}{6\sqrt{3}}+\frac{1}{3}\log 2.$$

9. Show that the curve defined by

$$y=0, \qquad \text{when } x=0,$$
$$y = x\sin\frac{1}{x}, \text{ when } 0<x\leqslant 1,$$

is continuous but not rectifiable.

10. Show that the curve defined by

$$y = 0, \qquad \text{when } x = 0,$$

$$y = x^2 \sin \frac{1}{x}, \text{ when } 0 < x \leqslant 1,$$

is rectifiable.

11. If $\Sigma_{mn} \equiv \dfrac{1}{mn} \sum\limits_{\substack{r=1,m \\ s=1,n}} f\left(\dfrac{r}{m}, \dfrac{s}{n}\right)$, where $f(x, y)$ is continuous with respect to the pair of variables (x, y) in the square

$$0 \leqslant x \leqslant 1 \text{ , } 0 \leqslant y \leqslant 1,$$

show that the limits

$$\lim_{\substack{m\to\infty \\ n\to\infty}} \Sigma_{mn}, \qquad \lim_{m\to\infty} \lim_{n\to\infty} \Sigma_{mn}, \qquad \lim_{n\to\infty} \lim_{m\to\infty} \Sigma_{mn}$$

exist and are equal.

Discuss the case where

$$f(x, y) \equiv \frac{1}{(1+xy)^2}.$$

12. If $f(x, y)$ is continuous with respect to the pair of variables (x, y) in the rectangle

$$a \leqslant x \leqslant b, \; c \leqslant y \leqslant d,$$

prove that

$$\int_a^b dx \int_c^d f(x, y) dy = (b-a)(d-c) f(\xi, \eta),$$

where (ξ, η) is a point of the rectangle.

INDEX

The numbers refer to page

PRINTED IN GREAT BRITAIN BY OLIVER AND BOYD LTD., EDINBURGH